In partnership with DiVI

AQA GCSE (9-1) Maths

Higher

Revision Guide

Author: Katie Wood

Series Editor: Naomi Bartholomew-Millar

The Oxford Revise GCSE Maths Series: Our approach

Our no-fuss approach lets you dive straight into exactly what you need to know for the exam. GCSE Grades and check-boxes help you monitor your own progress on every page, and you'll find plenty of further practice on the exact same page in the matching workbook. Best of all, our unique visual approach — with diagrams, mnemonics and handy memory tips — will help you recall even the trickiest points.

OXFORD
UNIVERSITY PRESS

Contents

Climb to 9 CLIMB TO 9

So you have the best possible chance of reaching Grade 9, we've carefully studied past exam papers and reports to identify the 7 trickiest question types.

CLIMB TO 9 Look for this logo to see which topics have most often caught students out in the past.

Pages 115-129: We've provided structured support on these pages for answering the 7 trickiest question types.

Use of calculators

This book provides support with both how and when to use your calculator. Look for these symbols against questions:

 Make sure to use your calculator – it's good practice for the exam.

Make sure not to use your calculator – this question would only appear in the non-calculator paper.

If there's no symbol, then the question could appear on either the calculator or the non-calculator paper.

Calculations

You need to be confident doing calculations with integers and decimals without a calculator.

Grade 3–4

Key points

- Use **BIDMAS** to remember the correct order of operations.
- Use these rules for multiplying with negative or positive numbers. The same rules work for division.

×	Positive	Negative
Positive	Positive	Negative
Negative	Negative	Positive

- Ensure you can accurately use written methods with integers and decimals.

Operations on the same level can be done either way around

Worked example

Grade 3

Work out

a) $-2 - 3(-2)^3$ **[2 marks]**

b) $3.7 + 8.16 \times 4.9$ **[3 marks]**

Solution

a) $-2 - 3(-2)^3 = -2 - 3(-8)$

$\qquad = -2 + 24$

$\qquad = 22$

$(-2)^3 = (-2) \times (-2) \times (-2)$
$= 4 \times (-2)$
$= -8$

b) To work out the multiplication, ignore the decimal points:

$816 \times 49 = 39\,984$, so $8.16 \times 4.9 = 39.984$

Now, work out the addition:

$$\begin{array}{r} 39.984 \\ + \ 3.700 \\ \hline 43.684 \\ {\scriptstyle 1 \ 1} \end{array}$$

$3.7 + 8.16 \times 4.9 = 43.684$

$$\begin{array}{r} 816 \\ \times \ 49 \\ \hline 7344 \\ 32640 \\ \hline 39984 \end{array}$$

Exam corner

Grade 3

1. Work out the value of $15 - 12\sqrt{34} + 9(-2)$

Circle the correct answer.

63   −11   15   −33   **[I got ___/1 mark]**

2. Beth is choosing between two mobile phone deals.

Grade 4

Deal 1	**Deal 2**
Initial cost of £97	No initial cost
£26.82 per month for 2 years	£20.35 per month for 3 years

Work out which deal is better value.   **[___/4 marks]**

Examiner's tip!

When working with decimals, use estimation (see page 3) to check your answers are sensible.

Rounding & truncation

You need to be able to round a number to a given number of decimal places or significant figures. Truncating a number is sometimes an alternative to rounding.

Use this flow-chart to help you round numbers.

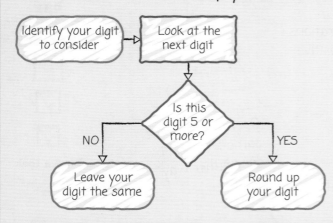

For example: try rounding 0.147 to 2 decimal places.

Your digit to consider is the 2nd decimal place, so 4

Look at the next digit, 7

YES, this is 5 or more.

Round up the 4 to a 5

Answer: 0.15

Key points

Significant figures

- To round to a number of significant figures, follow the usual rules of rounding in the flow-chart above.
- The first digit that is not 0 is the most significant.
- You might need to add zeros at the end of the number – check your answer makes sense.

Truncation

An alternative to rounding is **truncating** a number. This is where you just 'cut off' digits after the place value you are interested in. Examples are:
- Ages, e.g. if you are 15.7 years old, you say you are 15
- 'Real-life' division questions, e.g. if you are asked how many juice cartons can fit in a box, the answer might be 3 (but not 3.5).

Worked example

Grade 3

The answer to a calculation is 0.0287

a) Round the answer to 2 significant figures. **[1 mark]**

b) Truncate the answer to 2 decimal places. **[1 mark]**

Solution

a) 0.0287 = 0.029 to 2 significant figures

b) 0.0287 truncated to 2 decimal places is 0.02

Exam corner

Grade 3

1. The answer to a calculation is 62 357.92

   a) Round the answer to
      i) the nearest 1000   **ii)** 3 significant figures
      iii) 1 decimal place.   **[I got ___/3 marks]**

   b) Truncate the answer to an integer. **[___/1 mark]**

2. A recipe for eight identical cakes uses 2.25 kg of flour. How much flour is needed for one cake?
   Give your answer to 2 significant figures. **[___/2 marks]**

   Grade 3

Worked example

Grade 3

Work out the area of the rectangle. Give your answer to 3 significant figures.

[2 marks]

367 cm

89 cm

Solution

Area = 367 × 89

= 32 663

= 32 700 cm² to 3 significant figures

Estimation

A handy technique to quickly check whether a complex calculation is likely to be correct is to **estimate**.

Key points

- To estimate the value of a calculation:

  STEP 1: First round all the numbers (rounding to 1 sf often works best).

  STEP 2: Use BIDMAS to work out the estimated value.

- To estimate the square root of a number:

  STEP 1: Work out the two square numbers it lies between.

  STEP 2: Decide which of the square numbers it is closer to, then use this to give the estimate.

Worked example

Grade **4**

Estimate the value of $\dfrac{11 \times 5.7 - 23.4}{0.54}$

Show all your working. **[2 marks]**

Solution

First round each number to 1 significant figure.

$$\frac{11 \times 5.7 - 23.4}{0.54} \approx \frac{10 \times 6 - 20}{0.5}$$

$$= \frac{60 - 20}{0.5}$$

$$= \frac{40}{0.5}$$

$$= 80$$

To estimate the result of $562 \div 64.2$ round everything to 1 significant figure.

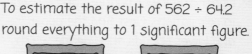

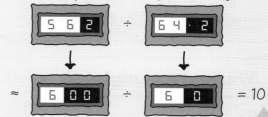

$$\approx \boxed{6\,0\,0} \div \boxed{6\,0} = 10$$

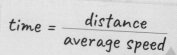

$$time = \frac{distance}{average\ speed}$$

Worked example

Grade **6**

Estimate the value of $\sqrt{76}$ to 1 decimal place. **[2 marks]**

Solution

76 is between 8^2 (= 64) and 9^2 (= 81).

76 is closer to 81 than 64

So $\sqrt{76}$ will be closer to 9 than 8

Give a sensible estimate:

$\sqrt{76} \approx 8.7$

(8.8 would also be a reasonable estimate.)

Exam corner

Grade **6**

1. The British Grand Prix has a lap length of 5.891 km and cars must complete 52 laps to finish the race.

   In one race, the average speed of the winning car was 204.2 km/h.

   Estimate the time the car took to complete the race.

   [I got ___/3 marks]

Grade **6**

2. Estimate the value of $\sqrt{125}$ to 1 decimal place.

   [___/2 marks]

Error intervals & bounds

The **error interval** of a number is the range of values it could have been before it was rounded.

Grade 5-7

Key points

- The **lower bound** of a measurement is the smallest value that would round to that measurement.
- The **upper bound** of a measurement is the smallest value that would <u>not</u> round to that measurement.
- The **error interval** for a measurement, m, is written:

  lower bound $\leq m <$ upper bound

- Upper and lower bounds can be used in calculations. First find the upper and lower bounds, then decide which you will need to use in the calculation.

3.7 has been **rounded** to 1 decimal place. What is the error interval?

Error interval is $3.65 \leq m < 3.75$, so m is greater than or equal to 3.65 but strictly less than 3.75 (3.75 would be rounded up).

3.7 has been **truncated** to 1 decimal place. What is the error interval?

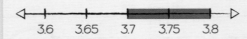

Error interval is $3.7 \leq m < 3.8$, so m is greater than or equal to 3.7 but strictly less than 3.8 (never actually equal to 3.8).

Confidence bar

Sorted!

☑

☑

☑

Had a look

  See page 2 for more on rounding and truncating.

Worked example
Grade 5

The mass of an apple, a g, is given as 80 g.
Give the error interval for a in each of these situations:

a) the mass was rounded to the nearest 10 g
b) the mass was rounded to the nearest integer
c) the mass was truncated to an integer.   **[1 mark each]**

Solution

a) $75 \leq a < 85$ b) $79.5 \leq a < 80.5$ c) $80 \leq a < 81$

Exam corner
Grade 6

1. The capacity, c ml, of a glass is given as 230 ml.

   Give the error interval for c in each of these situations.

   a) The capacity was rounded to the nearest ml.
   [I got ___/2 marks]

   b) The capacity was truncated to 2 significant figures.
   [___/2 marks]

2. A rectangle has length 18.5 cm and width 9.29 cm, each rounded to 3 significant figures.
Grade 7

   By considering bounds, work out the area of the rectangle to a suitable degree of accuracy. Give a reason for your answer.   **[___/5 marks]**

Worked example
Grade 7

 Consider the formula $a = \dfrac{F}{m}$

$F = 45$ to 2 significant figures and $m = 16.1$ to 3 significant figures.
By considering bounds, work out the value of a to a suitable degree of accuracy.   **[5 marks]**

Solution

Error intervals for F and m are:
$44.5 \leq F < 45.5$ and
$16.05 \leq m < 16.15$
Lower bound for a is given by:
$\dfrac{\text{lower bound of } F}{\text{upper bound of } m} = \dfrac{44.5}{16.15} = 2.755...$

Upper bound for a is given by:
$\dfrac{\text{upper bound of } F}{\text{lower bound of } m} = \dfrac{45.5}{16.05} = 2.834...$

Both the upper and lower bound of a round to 2.8
$a = 2.8$ to 2 significant figures

CLIMB TO 9 See pages 116-117 for more practice

Adding & subtracting fractions

You need to be able to add and subtract fractions given in different forms.

Grade 3-4

Key points

- You can **simplify** a fraction by dividing the numerator and denominator by the highest common factor (**HCF**).
- If the numerator is bigger than the denominator then the fraction is an **improper fraction**, e.g. $\frac{13}{6}$
- Improper fractions can be converted to **mixed numbers**, e.g. $\frac{13}{6} = 2\frac{1}{6}$
- You can only add or subtract fractions when the denominators are the same.

To add or subtract two fractions...

> Work out the lowest common multiple (**LCM**) of the denominators.

> Scale each fraction so they both have the LCM as their denominator.

> Add or subtract the numerators, but don't change the denominator.

Confidence bar

Sorted!

Had a look

Worked example

Grade 4

A jug contains $\frac{7}{8}$ litre of lemonade. How much lemonade is left in the jug after $\frac{1}{6}$ litre is poured out? **[3 marks]**

Solution

$\frac{7}{8} - \frac{1}{6} = \frac{21}{24} - \frac{4}{24}$ The LCM of 6 and 8 is 24

$\qquad\qquad = \frac{17}{24}$ $\frac{7}{8} = \frac{21}{24}$ and $\frac{1}{6} = \frac{4}{24}$

Subtract the numerators once the denominators are the same.

$\frac{17}{24}$ litre of lemonade is left in the jug.

Worked example

Grade 4

Two pipes of length $2\frac{3}{4}$ m and $1\frac{2}{3}$ m are joined end to end. How long is the new length of pipe? Give the answer as a mixed number. **[3 marks]**

Solution

$2\frac{3}{4} + 1\frac{2}{3} = \frac{11}{4} + \frac{5}{3}$ The LCM of 4 and 3 is 12

$\qquad\qquad = \frac{33}{12} + \frac{20}{12}$

$\qquad\qquad = \frac{53}{12}$

$\qquad\qquad = 4\frac{5}{12}$ Change to a mixed number.

The new length of pipe is $4\frac{5}{12}$ m.

Exam corner

Grade 4

1. A tub of sweets weighs $1\frac{8}{9}$ kg. An additional $\frac{5}{6}$ kg of sweets is added to the tub, then a child takes $\frac{1}{18}$ kg of sweets out of the tub. What does the tub of sweets weigh now? Give your answer as a mixed number in its simplest form. **[I got ___/4 marks]**

2. Work out the value of

Grade 4

   a) $\frac{9}{50} - \frac{11}{75}$ **[___/3 marks]**   b) $1\frac{1}{12} + \frac{8}{9}$ **[___/3 marks]**

Give your answers as fractions in their simplest form.

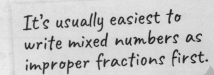

It's usually easiest to write mixed numbers as improper fractions first.

Examiner's tip!

Always use the LCM as the common denominator, otherwise the calculations could be much harder.

Multiplying & dividing fractions

You need to be able to multiply and divide fractions without using a calculator.

Key points

- To multiply two fractions, multiply the numerators and multiply the denominators.
- To divide by a fraction, multiply by its **reciprocal**.

  The **reciprocal** of a number is $\dfrac{1}{\text{number}}$.

- Make sure you cancel any common factors in the final answer.

You can use KFC to remember how to divide a fraction by another fraction:
Keep the first, Flip the other, and Change the sign:

so $\dfrac{2}{7} \div \dfrac{5}{6}$

Keep — Flip

Becomes $\left(\dfrac{2}{7}\right) \otimes \left(\dfrac{6}{5}\right)$

Change

Worked example

Grade 3

Work out these calculations and give your answers in their simplest form.

a) $\dfrac{3}{4}$ of $\dfrac{5}{6}$ **b)** $2\dfrac{7}{9} \times \dfrac{3}{10}$ **[5 marks]**

Solution

a) $\dfrac{3}{4}$ of $\dfrac{5}{6} = \dfrac{3}{4} \times \dfrac{5}{6}$

$= \dfrac{15}{24}$

$= \dfrac{5}{8}$ Cancel common factor of 3

Remember, of means multiply

b) $2\dfrac{7}{9} \times \dfrac{3}{10} = \dfrac{25}{9} \times \dfrac{3}{10}$ Convert $2\dfrac{7}{9}$ to an improper fraction.

$= \dfrac{75}{90}$

$= \dfrac{5}{6}$ Cancel common factor of 15

Convert mixed numbers to improper fractions first.

Worked example

Grade 3

Work out these calculations and give your answers in their simplest form.

a) $\dfrac{3}{8} \div \dfrac{7}{10}$ **b)** $5 \div \dfrac{1}{3}$ **[4 marks]**

Solution

a) $\dfrac{3}{8} \div \dfrac{7}{10} = \dfrac{3}{8} \times \dfrac{10}{7}$ Keep the $\dfrac{3}{8}$

Flip the $\dfrac{7}{10}$ to $\dfrac{10}{7}$

Change $\div$ to $\times$

$= \dfrac{30}{56}$

$= \dfrac{15}{28}$ Cancel common factor of 2

b) $5 \div \dfrac{1}{3} = 5 \times \dfrac{3}{1}$ Keep the 5

Flip the $\dfrac{1}{3}$ to $\dfrac{3}{1}$

Change $\div$ to $\times$

$= 5 \times 3$

$= 15$

You can think of an integer as a fraction over 1. So $3 = \dfrac{3}{1}$

Exam corner

Grade 3

1. Work out the value of $\dfrac{3}{4} \div \dfrac{5}{14}$

   Circle the correct answer.

   $2\dfrac{1}{10}$ $\dfrac{15}{56}$ $2\dfrac{1}{20}$ $\dfrac{10}{21}$ **[I got ___/1 mark]**

2. Jordan mixes orange squash and water in the ratio 2:7 **Grade 4**

   She uses $\dfrac{3}{8}$ litre of orange squash to make up a jugful.

   She pours the drink into cups each with a capacity of $\dfrac{3}{16}$ litre.

   Work out how many cups she fills. **[___/3 marks]**

Fractions, decimals & percentages

Fractions, decimals and percentages are different ways of writing the same number. You can convert between them without using a calculator.

Key points

You should learn these common fractions, decimals and percentages:

$\frac{1}{2} = 0.5 = 50\%$ $\frac{1}{4} = 0.25 = 25\%$

$\frac{1}{8} = 0.125 = 12.5\%$ $\frac{1}{5} = 0.2 = 20\%$

$\frac{1}{10} = 0.1 = 10\%$ $\frac{1}{3} = 0.\dot{3} = 33.\dot{3}\%$

$0.\dot{3}$ means $0.333333...$ and is called a **recurring decimal**.

Converting numbers

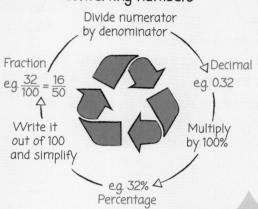

Divide numerator by denominator

Fraction e.g. $\frac{32}{100} = \frac{16}{50}$ → Decimal e.g. 0.32

Write it out of 100 and simplify

Multiply by 100%

e.g. 32% Percentage

See page 8 for how to convert a recurring decimal to a fraction.

Confidence bar

Sorted!

☑
☑
☑

Had a look

Worked example

 Write the fraction $\frac{5}{16}$ as a percentage.   **[3 marks]**

Solution

First convert to a decimal by dividing the numerator by the denominator:

$$16 \overline{\smash)5.^{5}0\,^{2}0\,^{4}0\,^{8}0} = 0.3125$$

Now multiply by 100% to convert to a percentage:

$0.3125 \times 100\% = 31.25\%$

So $\frac{5}{16} = 31.25\%$.

To decide if a fraction is a **terminating** or a **recurring** decimal:
- Simplify the fraction fully.
- Work out the prime factors of the denominator.
- If there are any prime factors other than 2 or 5, then the decimal will be recurring; otherwise, it will be terminating.

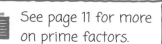
See page 11 for more on prime factors.

Worked example

a) Write $\frac{47}{40}$ as a percentage.   **[2 marks]**

b) Show that the fraction $\frac{26}{30}$ is a recurring decimal.   **[2 marks]**

Solution

a) $\frac{47}{40} = 1\frac{7}{40}$ So the percentage is over 100%.

$\frac{7}{40} = \frac{3.5}{20} = \frac{17.5}{100} = 17.5\%$

Therefore, $\frac{47}{40} = 117.5\%$.

b) First simplify the fraction fully: $\frac{26}{30} = \frac{13}{15}$

The denominator has prime factors 3 and 5

Therefore, it will be a recurring decimal.

Exam corner

1. Passengers on a train are travelling for work, school or leisure. $\frac{3}{8}$ of the passengers are travelling for work and 13% for school. Work out the percentage travelling for leisure.   **[I got __/3 marks]**

2. Use prime factors to show that $\frac{21}{98}$ is a recurring decimal.   **[__/2 marks]**

Recurring decimals

Recurring decimals have a repeating pattern in the digits after the decimal point. You can convert any recurring decimal to a fraction.

Key points

- A **rational number** can be written as a fraction. A number that cannot be written as a fraction is **irrational**.
- To convert a fraction to a decimal (recurring or terminating), divide the numerator by the denominator. You can stop as soon as you get a repeated digit (or group of digits) in the answer.
- To convert a recurring decimal to a fraction, use the strategy shown.

Converting a recurring decimal into a fraction in simple cases:

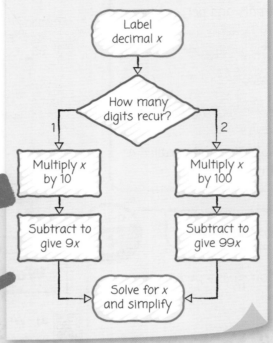

Label decimal x

How many digits recur?

1 → Multiply x by 10 → Subtract to give $9x$

2 → Multiply x by 100 → Subtract to give $99x$

Solve for x and simplify

Worked example

Grade 7

Write $0.\dot{7}\dot{2}$ as a fraction. **[2 marks]**

Solution

Let $x = 0.727272...$

Two digits recur, so

$100x = 72.727272...$

Subtract the equations:

$100x - x = 72.7272... - 0.7272...$

$99x = 72$

$x = \dfrac{72}{99}$

$x = \dfrac{8}{11}$

Worked example

Grade 8

Prove algebraically that $0.5\dot{8} = \dfrac{53}{90}$ **[2 marks]**

Solution

Let $x = 0.5888...$

$10x = 5.888...$

$100x = 58.888...$

$100x - 10x = 58.888... - 5.888...$

$90x = 53$

$x = \dfrac{53}{90}$

> This is slightly different – the first digit doesn't recur. Start by multiplying by 10, so only the recurring digits appear after the decimal point. Notice the denominator is 90. You'll need to get 90 on the left side of the equation, so subtracting $10x$ from $100x$.

Exam corner

Grade 7

1. **a)** Write $\dfrac{1}{7}$ as a decimal.
   [I got ___ /2 marks]

   b) Prove algebraically that $0.\dot{7} = \dfrac{7}{9}$
   [___ /2 marks]

Grade 8

2. Write $0.3\dot{2}\dot{4}$ as a fraction in its simplest form.
   [___ /3 marks]

Examiner's tip!

You might spot a pattern in questions such as these – but remember that when asked to 'prove', you have to show all the steps in your working.

> For Question 2, you'll need to multiply by 10 and 1000

Surds

A **surd** is an irrational square root. You can often simplify expressions involving surds.

Key points

- $\sqrt{ab} = \sqrt{a}\sqrt{b}$ and $\sqrt{\dfrac{a}{b}} = \dfrac{\sqrt{a}}{\sqrt{b}}$
- To simplify a surd, look for a factor that's a square number, e.g. $\sqrt{72} = \sqrt{36}\sqrt{2} = 6\sqrt{2}$
- Rewriting an expression without surds in the denominator is called **rationalising the denominator**. There are two different techniques you need to know for this.

Single surd in the denominator

Multiply numerator and denominator by the denominator, e.g. for $\dfrac{3}{\sqrt{5}}$, multiply by $\sqrt{5}$:

$$\frac{3\sqrt{5}}{\sqrt{5}\sqrt{5}} = \frac{3\sqrt{5}}{5}$$

Two terms in the denominator

Multiply numerator and denominator by the denominator with a changed sign, e.g. for $\dfrac{1}{2 + \sqrt{3}}$, multiply by $(2 - \sqrt{3})$:

$$\frac{(2 - \sqrt{3})}{(2 + \sqrt{3})(2 - \sqrt{3})} = \frac{(2 - \sqrt{3})}{4 - 3} = 2 - \sqrt{3}$$

This works because the denominator is
$(2 + \sqrt{3})(2 - \sqrt{3}) = 4 - \underbrace{2\sqrt{3} + 2\sqrt{3}}_{\text{these cancel out}} - 3$

Worked example

Grade **7**

Simplify fully $\sqrt{45} - \sqrt{32} + \sqrt{5}$

[2 marks]

Solution

First simplify each surd if possible:
$\sqrt{45} = \sqrt{9}\sqrt{5} = 3\sqrt{5}$
$\sqrt{32} = \sqrt{16}\sqrt{2} = 4\sqrt{2}$

Now collect like terms:
$$\sqrt{45} - \sqrt{32} + \sqrt{5} = 3\sqrt{5} - 4\sqrt{2} + \sqrt{5}$$
$$= 4\sqrt{5} - 4\sqrt{2}$$

This cannot be simplified any further.

Worked example

Grade **8**

 Express $\dfrac{1 + \sqrt{8}}{1 - \sqrt{2}}$ in the form $a + b\sqrt{2}$, where a and b are integers.

[3 marks]

Solution

$$\frac{1 + \sqrt{8}}{1 - \sqrt{2}} = \frac{(1 + \sqrt{8})(1 + \sqrt{2})}{(1 - \sqrt{2})(1 + \sqrt{2})}$$

$$= \frac{1 + \sqrt{2} + \sqrt{8} + \sqrt{16}}{1 - 2}$$

$$= \frac{1 + \sqrt{2} + 2\sqrt{2} + 4}{-1}$$

$$= \frac{5 + 3\sqrt{2}}{-1} = -5 - 3\sqrt{2}$$

$\sqrt{8} = \sqrt{4}\sqrt{2} = 2\sqrt{2}$

Remember: $\sqrt{2}\sqrt{8}$ equals $\sqrt{16}$

Exam corner

Grade **7**

1. Simplify fully
   a) $\sqrt{24}$ **[I got __/1 mark]**

   b) $\sqrt{98} - \sqrt{50}$ **[__/2 marks]**

   c) $\dfrac{6}{\sqrt{3}}$ **[__/2 marks]**

Grade **8**

2. Express $\dfrac{3 + \sqrt{7}}{3 - \sqrt{7}}$ in the form $a + b\sqrt{2}$, where a and b are integers. **[__/3 marks]**

Examiner's tip!

If you're told to write an expression in a certain form like this, it's another way of saying 'simplify' or 'rationalise the denominator' – so just follow the usual methods.

Index notation

A power of a number can also be called the **index** (plural **indices**). Indices can be positive or negative numbers including fractions.

Key points

INDEX LAWS

- Any number to the power 0 is 1
- If you multiply numbers with the same base, you add the powers.
- If you divide numbers with the same base, you subtract the powers.
- If you raise a power to another power, you multiply the powers.
- A power of -1 gives the reciprocal.
- A power of $\frac{1}{2}$ gives the square root.
- A power of $\frac{1}{n}$ gives the nth root.

EXAMPLES

$7^0 = 1$

$7^5 \times 7^3 = 7^8$

$7^5 \div 7^3 = 7^2$

$(7^5)^3 = 7^{15}$

$7^{-1} = \frac{1}{7}$

$49^{\frac{1}{2}} = 7$

$49^{\frac{1}{4}} = \sqrt{7}$

$\text{BASE}^{\text{index}}$

7^5

In the number 7^5

7 is the base

5 is the power or index

If there is no power, assume it to be 1, so $5 = 5^1$

Worked example

Grade 6

Write $\sqrt{5^3 \div 5^{-5}}$ in simplified index form. **[2 marks]**

Solution

$\sqrt{5^3 \div 5^{-5}} = \sqrt{5^8}$ First subtract the powers within the square root: $3 - -5 = 8$

$= (5^8)^{\frac{1}{2}}$ Write the root as a power.

$= 5^4$ Multiply the powers: $8 \times \frac{1}{2} = 4$

Worked example

Work out the value of

a) $\left(\frac{9}{4}\right)^{\frac{1}{2}}$ **[1 mark]**

b) $64^{-\frac{2}{3}}$ **[3 marks]**

If you have a negative power, write it using brackets like this with a power of -1 on the outside.

Solution

a) $\left(\frac{9}{4}\right)^{\frac{1}{2}} = \frac{\sqrt{9}}{\sqrt{4}} = \frac{3}{2}$

b) $64^{-\frac{2}{3}} = \left(64^{\frac{2}{3}}\right)^{-1}$

$= (4^2)^{-1}$ Work out the root first: $64^{\frac{1}{3}} = \sqrt[3]{64} = 4$

$= 16^{-1}$

$= \frac{1}{16}$ A power of -1 gives the reciprocal.

When dealing with fractions, you can apply the power to the numerator and the denominator separately.

Grade 7

Exam corner

Grade 7

1. Work out the value of $\left(\frac{3}{5}\right)^{-2}$

Circle the correct answer.

$\frac{9}{25}$ $\frac{6}{5}$ $\frac{25}{9}$ $\frac{5}{6}$

[I got ___/1 mark]

Grade 8

2. $\sqrt{8} = 2^n$

Work out the value of n **[___/3 marks]**

Prime factor decomposition

A number is **prime** if it has exactly two factors: itself and 1. Every whole number can be written as a **product of prime factors** in a unique way.

Key points

To write a number as a **product of prime factors**:

- Use a factor tree to split the number into pairs of factors.
- Each time you reach a prime number, circle it and move to another number.
- Write out the number as a product, using index form.
- This is also called the **prime factor decomposition** of the number.

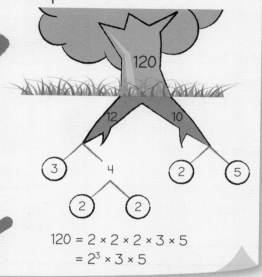

Working out the prime factor decomposition of 120

$$120 = 2 \times 2 \times 2 \times 3 \times 5$$
$$= 2^3 \times 3 \times 5$$

Confidence bar

Sorted!

☑
☑
☑

Had a look

Worked example

Grade 4

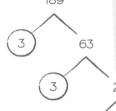
Write 189 as a product of its prime factors. **[2 marks]**

Solution

189
3, 63
3, 21
3, 7

Remember this...
1 is not a prime number!

$$189 = 3 \times 3 \times 3 \times 7$$
$$= 3^3 \times 7$$

Try finding the prime factors of 189 by completing this factor tree instead:

189
21, 9

Your final answer should be the same.

Worked example

Grade 5

The prime factor decomposition of a number is:
$$2^3 \times 3 \times 5 \times 7^2$$
Show whether the number is a multiple of

a) 7   b) 10   c) 9   **[3 marks]**

Solution

a) Yes, the number is a multiple of 7, since 7 is a prime factor.

b) Yes, the number is a multiple of 10, since both 2 and 5 are prime factors and 2 × 5 = 10

c) No, the number is not a multiple of 9, since 9 is not a factor (3 is a prime factor but 3^2 is not).

Exam corner

1. Write these numbers as a product of their prime factors. Use index notation.

   a) 54 **[I got ___/2 marks]**   b) 650 **[___/2 marks]**

   Grade 4

2. A number is a multiple of 6, 14 and 50. What is the smallest possible value of the number? Write your answer using prime factors. **[___/2 marks]**

   Grade 5

Working out HCF and LCM

You can use prime factors to work out the highest common factor (HCF) or the lowest common multiple (LCM). This is very useful for big numbers.

Key points

To find the HCF and the LCM of two numbers:

STEP 1: Work out all the prime factors.

STEP 2: Draw a Venn diagram showing the prime factors of both numbers.

STEP 3:

- Multiply the numbers in the intersection to find the HCF.
- Multiply the numbers in the union (i.e. all the numbers shown) to find the LCM.

Working out the HCF & LCM of 150 and 225

Step 1: $150 = 2 \times 3 \times 5 \times 5$
$225 = 3 \times 3 \times 5 \times 5$

Step 2:

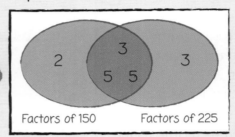

Factors of 150   Factors of 225

Step 3: $HCF = 3 \times 5 \times 5 = 75$
$LCM = 2 \times 3 \times 5 \times 5 \times 3 = 450$

Confidence bar

Sorted!

☑

☑

☑

Had a look

Worked example

Two numbers have prime factor decomposition $2^2 \times 3 \times 5^2$ and $2^3 \times 5 \times 11^2$

Work out

a) the highest common factor   **[3 marks]**

b) the lowest common multiple.   **[2 marks]**

Leave your answers in index form.

Grade 5

Solution

Draw a Venn diagram to show the prime factors.

a) $HCF = 2 \times 2 \times 5$
$= 2^2 \times 5$

b) $LCM = 5 \times 3 \times 2 \times 2 \times 5 \times 2 \times 11 \times 11$
$= 2^3 \times 3 \times 5^2 \times 11^2$

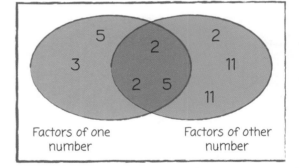

Factors of one number   Factors of other number

Exam corner

1. $A = 3 \times 5^2 \times 13$ and $B = 3^2 \times 13^2 \times 17^2$

   a) Work out the highest common factor of A and B **[I got ___ /3 marks]**

   b) Work out the lowest common multiple of A and B **[___ /2 marks]**

Leave your answers in index form.

Grade 5

2. The Venn diagram shows the prime factors of two numbers N and P
The highest common factor of the two numbers is 14
The lowest common multiple of the two number is 420
Work out the two numbers N and P **[___ /4 marks]**

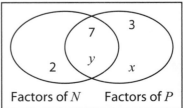

Factors of N Factors of P

Grade 5

Standard form

You can use a power of 10 to write a very large or a very small number in standard form. This makes it easier to understand the size of the number.

Grade 3-4

Key points

Standard form is written in this way:

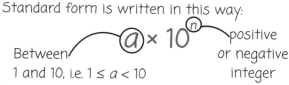

Between 1 and 10, i.e. $1 \le a < 10$

$@ \times 10^n$

positive or negative integer

Converting from standard form to ordinary number:

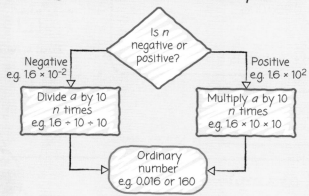

Is n negative or positive?

Negative e.g. 1.6×10^{-2}

Divide a by 10 n times e.g. $1.6 \div 10 \div 10$

Positive e.g. 1.6×10^2

Multiply a by 10 n times e.g. $1.6 \times 10 \times 10$

Ordinary number e.g. 0.016 or 160

Converting from ordinary number to standard form:

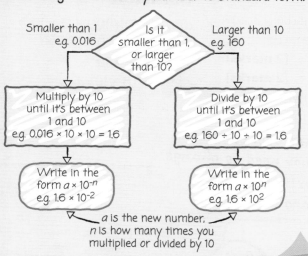

Smaller than 1 e.g. 0.016

Is it smaller than 1, or larger than 10?

Larger than 10 e.g. 160

Multiply by 10 until it's between 1 and 10 e.g. $0.016 \times 10 \times 10 = 1.6$

Divide by 10 until it's between 1 and 10 e.g. $160 \div 10 \div 10 = 1.6$

Write in the form $a \times 10^{-n}$ e.g. 1.6×10^{-2}

Write in the form $a \times 10^n$ e.g. 1.6×10^2

a is the new number, n is how many times you multiplied or divided by 10

Worked example

Grade 3

Write these as ordinary numbers.

a) 5.06×10^5

b) 1.7×10^{-3} **[2 marks]**

Solution

a) Multiply by 10, 5 times:
$5.06 \times 10^5 = 506\,000$

b) Divide by 10, 3 times:
$1.7 \times 10^{-3} = 0.0017$

Remember this...

A positive power gives a big number.
A negative power gives a small number (**not** a negative number).

Worked example

Grade 4

Write these numbers in standard form.

a) 0.000 324   b) 6 941 000   **[2 marks]**

Solution

Work out how many times you need to multiply or divide the number by 10 get it between 1 and 10

a) You multiply 0.000 324 by 10 four times to get 3.24, so $0.000\,324 = 3.24 \times 10^{-4}$

b) You divide 6 941 000 by 10 six times to get 6.941, so $6\,941\,000 = 6.941 \times 10^6$

Exam corner

Grade 4

1. The length of a bacterial cell is 2.01×10^{-6} metres.
   Write the length in metres as an ordinary number.
   Circle the correct answer.
   0.000 000 201 m   0.000 002 01 m   0.000 0201 m   2 010 000 m **[I got __ /1 mark]**

2. The average distance between Saturn and Uranus is 1.45×10^9 km.
   The average distance between Saturn and Jupiter is 64 600 000 km.
   Show whether Uranus or Jupiter is closer to Saturn. **[__ /2 marks]**

Grade 4

Examiner's tip!

Check your answers by doing the reverse, e.g. put ordinary numbers back into standard form.

Calculating with standard form

You need to practise the methods of adding, subtracting, multiplying and dividing numbers in standard form.

Key points

- To add or subtract numbers in standard form, convert to ordinary numbers first.
- To multiply or divide numbers in standard form, regroup then use index laws.

To multiply or divide numbers in standard form:

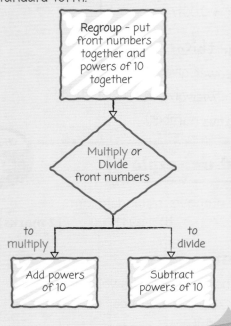

Regroup – put front numbers together and powers of 10 together

Multiply or Divide front numbers

to multiply → Add powers of 10

to divide → Subtract powers of 10

Worked example

Grade 5

Work out the value of
$8.9 \times 10^{-4} - 6 \times 10^{-6}$
Give your answer in standard form.

[2 marks]

Solution

$8.9 \times 10^{-4} = 0.00089$

$6 \times 10^{-6} = 0.000006$

$$\begin{array}{r} 0.000890 \\ -0.000006 \\ \hline 0.000884 \end{array}$$ which is 8.84×10^{-4}

 See page 10 for more on index laws.

Confidence bar

Sorted!

☑
☑
☑

Had a look

Worked example

Grade 5

Given that
$a = 6 \times 10^5$ and $b = 3 \times 10^{-2}$,
work out the value of
a) ab **[2 marks]**
b) $a \div b$ **[2 marks]**
Give your answers in standard form.

Solution

a) $ab = (6 \times 10^5) \times (3 \times 10^{-2})$
$= (6 \times 3) \times (10^{5-2})$
$= 18 \times 10^3$
$= 1.8 \times 10^4$

b) $a \div b = (6 \times 10^5) \div (3 \times 10^{-2})$
$= (6 \div 3) \times (10^{5-(-2)})$
$= 2 \times 10^7$

18 is not between 1 and 10 so you need to change this further to get standard form.

Exam corner

Grade 6

1. Work out the value and give your answers in standard form:
   a) $4.2 \times 10^7 - 6.1 \times 10^6$ **[I got __/3 marks]**
   b) $(9 \times 10^{-7}) \times (8 \times 10^5)$ **[__ /3 marks]**
   c) $(2.4 \times 10^{-7}) \div (9.6 \times 10^{-5})$ **[__ /3 marks]**
   d) $(7.7 \times 10^5) \div (1.1 \times 10^{-3}) \times (3 \times 10^4)$ **[__ /3 marks]**

2. The area of Wales is approximately $2.1 \times 10^4 \text{ km}^2$
   The population of Wales is approximately 3×10^6
   Work out the average area per person, giving your answer as an ordinary number.   **[__ /3 marks]**

Grade 6

In Question 1 part a, if you're feeling confident, you could write both numbers with the same power of 10, instead of converting into ordinary numbers. Use 10^7

Simplifying expressions

Algebraic expressions can be simplified in different ways, including **collecting like terms** and using **index laws**.

Grade

3–7

Key points

- An **expression** is a collection of letters and numbers, e.g. $2a - 5$
- Each part of an expression is called a **term**, e.g. $2a$ and 5 are terms.
- The **coefficient** of a term is the number part, e.g. 2 is the coefficient of the term $2a$
- You can simplify expressions by adding or subtracting the **like terms**.
- You can also use **index laws** to simplify:

$$a^m \times a^n = a^{m+n} \qquad a^m \div a^n = a^{m-n} \qquad (a^m)^n = a^{m \times n}$$

$$a^{-1} = \frac{1}{a} \qquad a^0 = 1 \qquad a^{\frac{1}{n}} = \sqrt[n]{a}$$

Remember this...

$$\underbrace{8 + 7x - 5y}_{\text{expression}} \overbrace{= x - \frac{x}{2}}^{\text{expression}}$$

equation

term   term   term   term   term

Confidence bar

Sorted!

☑
☑
☑

Had a look

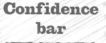

See page 10 for more on index laws.

Worked example **Grade 5**

Simplify

a) $\dfrac{12s^5t^2}{24st^7}$ **b)** $(3rs^2)^3$ **[2 marks each]**

Solution

a) Consider the coefficients: $\dfrac{12}{24} = \dfrac{1}{2}$

Consider s: $\dfrac{s^5}{s} = s^4$

Consider t: $\dfrac{t^2}{t^7} = t^{-5} = \dfrac{1}{t^5}$

$\dfrac{12s^5t^2}{24st^7} = \dfrac{s^4}{2t^5}$ or you could write $\dfrac{1}{2}s^4t^{-5}$

b) Remember to consider the coefficient: $3^3 = 27$

Now consider r and s:

$(3rs^2)^3 = 27r^3s^6$

Worked example **Grade 7**

Work out the value of x when $\sqrt{\dfrac{5^2 \times 5^4}{5^7}} = \dfrac{1}{5}^x$

[4 marks]

Solution

Since a power of $\frac{1}{2}$ gives the square root:

$$\sqrt{\frac{5^2 \times 5^4}{5^7}} = \left(\frac{5^2 \times 5^4}{5^7}\right)^{\frac{1}{2}}$$

$$= \left(\frac{5^6}{5^7}\right)^{\frac{1}{2}}$$

$$= (5^{-1})^{\frac{1}{2}} = \left(\frac{1}{5}\right)^{\frac{1}{2}}$$

$$\left(\frac{1}{5}\right)^{\frac{1}{2}} = \frac{1}{5}^x$$

Therefore $x = \dfrac{1}{2}$

Exam corner **Grade 4**

1. Write an expression for

a) the perimeter of the T-shape   **[I got __/2 marks]**

b) the area of the T-shape.   **[__/2 marks]**

Give your answers in their simplest form.

$3x$ cm

y cm

x cm

$5y$ cm

x cm

See page 74 for more on area and perimeter.

2. Simplify **Grade 6**

a) $a^3 \times a^5$ **[__/1 mark]**   **b)** $a^3b^2 \div ab^3$ **[__/2 marks]**

c) $(2a^3b)^4$ **[__/2 marks]**   **d)** $\sqrt{9a^4b^2c^{-6}}$ **[__/2 marks]**

CLIMB TO 9 See pages 120–121 for more practice.

Solving linear equations

An equation such as $3x + 2 = 10$ or $2x + 5 = 8 + x$ is called a linear equation. You can solve it using the balance method.

Key points

- Use the **balance method** to solve equations. This means always doing the **same thing** to both **sides** of the equation.
- If an equation has an unknown term on both sides, first change the equation so the unknown term appears on only one side.
- If an equation involves a fraction, multiply both sides by its denominator.

To solve the equation $2x + 5 = 8 + x$:

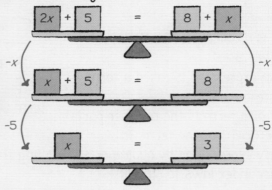

The solution is $x = 3$

Worked example

Solve $\dfrac{3 - 2x}{4} = x$ **[3 marks]**

Solution

$\dfrac{3 - 2x}{4} \times 4 = x \times 4$ Multiply both sides by the denominator.

$3 - 2x = 4x$

$3 - 2x + 2x = 4x + 2x$ Add $2x$ to both sides.

$3 = 6x$

$\dfrac{3}{6} = \dfrac{6x}{6}$ Divide both sides by 6

$\dfrac{1}{2} = x$

This is the same as writing $x = \dfrac{1}{2}$

Exam corner

1. Solve

   a) $3x + 6 = 20 - 4x$ **[I got ___/2 marks]**

   b) $\dfrac{x + 6}{5} = 8$ **[___/2 marks]**

   c) $\dfrac{3x}{4} - 3 = 9$ **[___/2 marks]**

2. Lucy thinks of a number, multiplies it by 4 and adds 15. The result is the same as when she subtracts her original number from 5

   Form and solve an equation to find Lucy's number.   **[___/3 marks]**

Worked example

The square and the triangle have the same perimeter.

 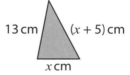

13 cm $(x + 5)$ cm

x cm x cm

Form an equation and solve it to find the value of x **[4 marks]**

Solution

Perimeter of square = $4x$

Perimeter of triangle = $x + (x + 5) + 13 = 2x + 18$

The equation is $4x = 2x + 18$

$4x - 2x = 2x - 2x + 18$ Subtract $2x$

$2x = 18$

$\dfrac{2x}{2} = \dfrac{18}{2}$ Divide by 2

$x = 9$

Start by adding 3 to both sides of the equation, so the fraction is on its own on one side of the equation.

CLIMB TO 9   See pages 118–119 for more practice

Linear graphs

A **linear** graph is a straight line, which can be vertical, horizontal or sloping.

Key points

- The equation of a graph is a rule that is true for all the points on the graph.
- You can use a table of values to find points on the graph.
- Equations such as $y = 3$ are horizontal lines.
- Equations such as $x = 3$ are vertical lines.
- Equations such as $y = x$ and $y = 2x + 5$ are sloping lines.
- The **gradient** of a straight line is a measure of its slope. Identify two points on the line where you can read the exact coordinates, then:

$$\text{Gradient} = \frac{\text{vertical change}}{\text{horizontal change}}$$

- A line through the origin with gradient m has equation $y = mx$

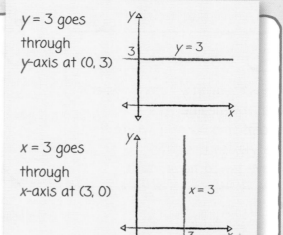

$y = 3$ goes through y-axis at $(0, 3)$

$x = 3$ goes through x-axis at $(3, 0)$

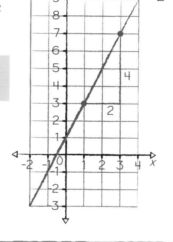

$\text{Gradient} = \frac{4}{2} = 2$

Remember this...

A gradient can be positive or negative.

 uphill

Positive gradient when you **P**ush uphill

 downhill

Negative gradient points downhill

Exam corner

Grade 4

1. Work out the gradient of the line shown and write the equation of the line.

   [I got ___/2 marks]

2. The points $A(-2, -5)$ and $B(4, -7)$ are on a line L

   a) Work out the gradient of L **[___/1 mark]**

   The point $C(7, a)$ is also on L

   b) Work out the value of a **[___/2 marks]**

Grade 5

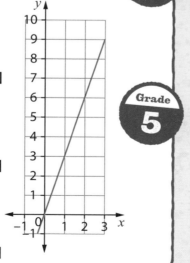

Worked example

Grade 4

Draw the graph of $y = -\frac{1}{2}x$ **[2 marks]**

Solution

This is a line through the origin with a gradient of $-\frac{1}{2}$

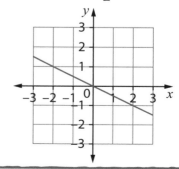

Equations of linear graphs

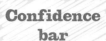

You need to be able to work out the equation of a straight line, and identify the gradient and y-intercept from an equation.

Key points

- A straight line has equation. $y = mx + c$ where
  m is the gradient of the line,
  c is the **y-intercept** (the number where the line crosses the y-axis).
- Parallel lines have the same gradient.

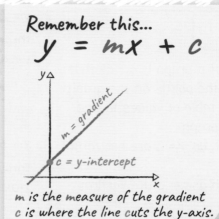

Remember this...

$$y = mx + c$$

m is the measure of the gradient
c is where the line cuts the y-axis.

Confidence bar

Sorted!

☑
☑
☑

Had a look

Worked example

Grade 4

A line has equation $2y + 6 = 4x$.
Work out the gradient and the y-intercept of the line. **[3 marks]**

Solution

Rearrange the equation so it's in the form $y = mx + c$:

$2y + 6 - 6 = 4x - 6$

$2y = 4x - 6$

$\dfrac{2y}{2} = \dfrac{4x - 6}{2}$

$y = 2x - 3$

The gradient is 2 and the y-intercept is -3

Worked example

Grade 5

A line passes through the points (1, 2) and (4, –7). Work out the equation of the line. **[3 marks]**

Solution

First, draw a sketch to find the gradient.

$\text{Gradient} = \dfrac{\text{change in } y}{\text{change in } x}$

$= \dfrac{-9}{3} = -3$

So far, you know the equation is $y = -3x + c$

To find the value of c, substitute the coordinate pair (1, 2) into the equation:

$2 = -3 \times 1 + c$

$2 = -3 + c$

$c = 5$

The equation is $y = -3x + 5$

> A line sloping from top left down to bottom right will have a negative gradient.

Exam corner

Grade 4

1. The equations of four lines are given:

   $y = 5x + 1 \quad y + 5x = 3 \quad 2y = 10x - 1 \quad 2y + 1 = 5x$

   a) Which two lines are parallel? **[I got __/2 marks]**

   b) Which two lines have the same y-intercept? **[__/2 marks]**

2. Work out the equation of each of these lines.

   a) A line that passes through the point (0, –3) and has gradient 5 **[__/1 mark]**

   b) A line that passes through the points (0, 5) and (4, 7) **[__/3 marks]**

   c) A line that passes through the points (1, 3) and (2, 1) **[__/4 marks]**

Grade 5

> Parallel lines have the same gradient, so rearrange each equation to find the gradient of the line.

Perpendicular lines

You can use the fact that perpendicular lines meet at a right angle to find their gradients.

Key points

If two lines are perpendicular, then the gradient of one line is the **negative reciprocal** of the gradient of the other line.

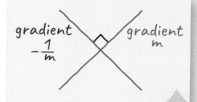

gradient $-\dfrac{1}{m}$ gradient m

Worked example

Grade 7

A line, L, has equation $2y - x + 2 = 0$

Work out the equation of the line that is perpendicular to L and passes through the point $(5, -4)$.   **[4 marks]**

To find the gradient of a perpendicular line:

flip and **switch**

find the reciprocal   change the sign

e.g. if the gradient of a line is 5:

flip and **switch**

$5 \rightarrow \dfrac{1}{5} \rightarrow -\dfrac{1}{5}$

The gradient of the perpendicular line is $-\dfrac{1}{5}$

Solution

The first step is to rearrange the equation of L to the form $y = mx + c$:

$2y - x + 2 = 0$

$2y = x - 2$

$y = \dfrac{1}{2}x - 1$

Gradient of $L = \dfrac{1}{2}$

Flip to 2 then **switch** to -2

So far you know equation is $y = -2x + c$

To find the value of c, substitute the coordinate pair $(5, -4)$ into the equation:

$-4 = -2(5) + c$

$-4 = -10 + c$

$c = 6$

The equation is $y = -2x + 6$

To show that lines are perpendicular, demonstrate that the product of the gradients is −1

Exam corner

1. A line, L, has equation $9y - 3x = 2$ **Grade 6**

   a) Work out the y-intercept of L

[I got ___/1 mark]

   b) Show that

   i) $y - \dfrac{1}{3}x = 4$ is parallel to L **[___/1 mark]**

   ii) $y + 3x = 4$ is perpendicular to L

[___/2 marks]

2. A line, L_1, has equation $y = -\dfrac{2}{3}x + 2$ **Grade 7**

   a) Draw the graph of L_1 for $-6 \leq x \leq 6$

[___/2 marks]

   The line L_2 is perpendicular to L_1 and passes through $(-8, 1)$.

   b) Work out the equation of L_2 **[___/3 marks]**

Linear inequalities

In an inequality, the left-hand side is not necessarily equal to the right-hand side but can be less than or greater than it. The solution to an inequality is usually a range of values.

Key points

- You can solve an inequality by treating the inequality sign like an equals sign and using the balance method.
- The one difference to remember: do not multiply or divide by a negative number because this would affect the direction of the inequality sign.
- The solution to an inequality can be shown on a number line or by using set notation, e.g. $\{x : x > 6\}$.

See page 16 for the balance method.

See page 112 for more on set notation.

A hollow circle shows that the number is <u>not</u> included.

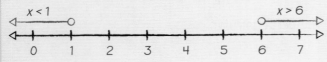

A filled-in circle shows that the number <u>is</u> included.

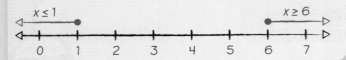

Worked example

Grade 5

a) Solve the inequality $8 - 2x > 12$ **[3 marks]**

b) Display the solution to part **a** on a number line.   **[1 mark]**

Solution

a) $8 - 2x > 12$ You want the $2x$ term to be positive, so start by adding $2x$

$8 > 12 + 2x$

$-4 > 2x$

$-2 > x$ or $x < -2$

b)
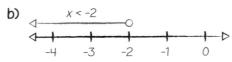

Exam corner

Grade 5

1. Solve these inequalities and display the solutions on number lines.

   a) $x + 9 > 12$ **[I got___/2 marks]**

   b) $-3x \le 12$ **[___/3 marks]**

   c) $2x + 13 \ge 25$ **[___/3 marks]**

Grade 6

2. $x - 3 < 2x + 5$ and $12 - 5x > 7$

   a) Work out the set of values of x which satisfies both the inequalities. **[___/4 marks]**

   b) Display the solution on a number line.   **[___/1 mark]**

   c) Write all possible integer values of x **[___/1 mark]**

Worked example

Grade 6

Work out the set of values of x for which
$-3 < 5x + 1 \le 7$ **[3 marks]**

Solution

Consider each part separately:

$-3 < 5x + 1$ and $5x + 1 \le 7$

$-4 < 5x$ $5x \le 6$

$-\dfrac{4}{5} < x$ $x \le \dfrac{6}{5}$

Set of values is $\left\{ x: -\dfrac{4}{5} < x \le \dfrac{6}{5} \right\}$

Regions on graphs

Inequalities involving two variables can be shown as regions on a graph.

Key points

To represent the solutions to inequalities on a graph:

STEP 1: Write each inequality as an equation and draw the graph.
Draw **strict inequalities** (< and >) with a **dotted line**.

STEP 2: Work out which side of the line you need.

STEP 3: Shade the region that satisfies ALL the inequalities in the question.

Worked example

Grade 7

Shade the region that satisfies the inequalities $y > 4 - 2x$, $x \leq 7$ and $y \leq 3$ **[4 marks]**

Solution

STEP 1: Draw the lines $y = 4 - 2x$, $x = 7$ and $y = 3$

$y = 4 - 2x$ will be **dotted** since there are no solutions on the line.

STEP 2: It's easy to see that $x \leq 7$ means you need the area to the left of the line $x = 7$

Similarly, $y \leq 3$ means the area below the line $y = 3$

Now consider $y > 4 - 2x$. Pick a point on one side of the line and check if it satisfies the inequality:

e.g. pick (0, 0): it is NOT true that $0 \geq 4 - 2(0)$

Therefore, you must need the area that does not include (0, 0).

STEP 3: Shade the area that satisfies all the inequalities.

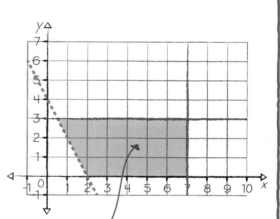

Exam corner

Grade 6

1. Write an inequality to describe the shaded region on each graph.

a)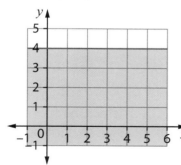

b)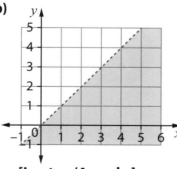

[I got ___/4 marks]

2. a) Shade the region that satisfies the inequalities
   $x + y \geq 2$, $y < 2x$, $x \leq 3$ **[___/3 marks]**

   Grade 7

   b) Nathan claims that the point (2, 4) is in the region. Is he correct? Give a reason for your answer. **[___/1 mark]**

Worked example

Grade 6

Write an inequality to describe the shaded region. **[2 marks]**

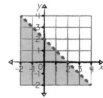

Solution

The line has gradient –1 and y-intercept 2. So its equation is $y = -(1)x + 2$ or $y = 2 - x$

Dotted line means strict inequality, and the shading is under the line so: $y < 2 - x$

Check this works for (0, 0):

$0 < 2 - 0$ ✓

Linear simultaneous equations

Two equations involving two variables (such as *x* and *y*) that you want to solve together are called **simultaneous equations**.

Key points

You can use the **elimination method** to solve simultaneous equations:

STEP 1: Number the equations (1) and (2).

STEP 2: Multiply one or both equations (if necessary) by a number.

STEP 3: Add or subtract the equations to eliminate one of the variables.

STEP 4: Solve your new equation to find the value of one variable.

STEP 5: Substitute this value into one of the original equations. Solve to find the other variable.

At **STEP 3**, use the STOP method:

Same Take Opposite Plus

If the sign is the Same then Take away (i.e. subtract the equations).

 See page 37 for how graphs can be used to solve simultaneous equations.

Confidence bar

Sorted!

☑
☑
☑

Had a look

Exam corner

1. The perimeter of the rectangle is 28 cm and the perimeter of the triangle is 22 cm.

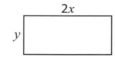 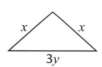

a) Form a pair of simultaneous equations.
   [I got __/2 marks]

b) Work out the value of *x* and *y*
   [__/3 marks]

 2. The cost of five bottles of milk and two packs of cheese is £10.30. The cost of two bottles of milk and three packs of cheese is £10.94. Form and solve simultaneous equations to find the price of a bottle of milk and the price of a pack of cheese.
   [__/4 marks]

Examiner's tip!

Always check your values of *x* and *y* by substituting into the original equations.

Worked example

 The cost of three adult tickets and two child tickets to a theme park is £155

The cost of two adult tickets and five child tickets is £195

a) Form a pair of simultaneous equations to describe this situation. **[2 marks]**

b) Solve your equations to find the cost of an adult ticket and the cost of a child ticket. **[3 marks]**

Solution

a) Use *a* = cost of adult ticket and *c* = cost of child ticket.

The equations are $3a + 2c = 155$ (1)
and $2a + 5c = 195$ (2)

b) Multiply (1) by 2: $6a + 4c = 310$ (3)
Multiply (2) by 3: $6a + 15c = 585$ (4)

Using the STOP method, both of the 6a terms are positive so subtract the equations ('Same Take')

(4) − (3): $11c = 275$

$c = 25$

Substitute into equation (1): $3a + 50 = 155$

$3a = 105$ so $a = 35$

The cost of an adult ticket is £35 and the cost of a child ticket is £25

See pages 118–119 for more practice

CLIMB TO 9

Expanding brackets

When you **expand** brackets you multiply the expressions to remove the brackets.

Key points

- **Single brackets:** multiply each term inside the brackets by the term in front of the brackets.
- **Double brackets:** multiply all terms in the first set of brackets by all terms in the second set of brackets. Then simplify if possible.
- **Triple brackets:** multiply the first two and simplify, then multiply by the third.

Worked example

Expand and simplify fully
$x(2x + y) - 3y(1 - x)$ **[3 marks]**

Solution

Expand each pair of brackets:

$x(2x + y) = 2x^2 + xy$

$-3y(1 - x) = -3y + 3xy$

Now simplify by collecting like terms:

$2x^2 \boxed{+ xy} - 3y \boxed{+ 3xy} = 2x^2 + 4xy - 3y$

Remember this...

If there are two terms in each set of brackets, use the FOIL method:

First - multiply the First term in each bracket.

Outer - multiply the Outer two terms.

Inner - multiply the Inner two terms.

Last - multiply the Last term in each bracket.

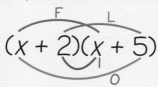

$(x + 2)(x + 5)$

Worked example

Expand and fully simplify
a) $(3 + y)(1 - 2y)$ **[2 marks]**
b) $(x + 1)(x + 2)(x + 3)$ **[4 marks]**

Solution

a) Use FOIL or a multiplication grid:

$(3 + y)(1 - 2y)$

×	3	y
1	3	y
-2y	-6y	-2y²

$= 3 + y - 6y - 2y^2$

$= 3 - 5y - 2y^2$

b) Use FOIL or a multiplication grid to expand the first two sets of brackets:

$(x + 1)(x + 2) = x^2 + 2x + x + 2$
$= x^2 + 3x + 2$

Now multiply this by the third set of brackets. You could use a multiplication grid, or just be systematic and multiply every term in the first bracket by every term in the second:

$(x^2 + 3x + 2)(x + 3) = x^3 + 3x^2 + 3x^2 + 9x + 2x + 6$

$= x^3 + 6x^2 + 11x + 6$

Exam corner

1. Write an expression for the area of this shape. Give your answer in its simplest form.
   [I got __/3 marks]

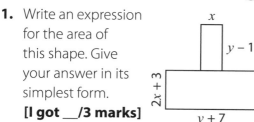

2. Expand and fully simplify

   a) $(3x + 2)^2$ **[__/2 marks]**

   b) $(2x - 1)(x + 1)(3x + 2)$ **[__/4 marks]**

There should be 6 terms, because there are 3 in the first brackets and 2 in the second, so 3 × 2 = 6 combinations.

CLIMB TO 9 See pages 118-121 for more practice.

Factorising 1

Factorising is the opposite of expanding brackets.

Grade 4–5

Key points

- You can sometimes factorise an expression by writing the HCF in front of the brackets then working out what must go inside,
  e.g. $6x + 9y = 3(2x + 3y)$

- To factorise an expression $x^2 + bx + c$:
  STEP 1: Draw brackets and write x in each: $(x \quad)(x \quad)$

  STEP 2: Identify two numbers (positive or negative) **that add to give b and multiply to give c**

  STEP 3: Write these numbers in, then check your answer by expanding the brackets.

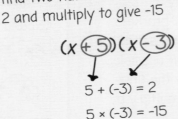

To factorise $x^2 + 2x - 15$,
find two numbers that add to give 2 and multiply to give –15

$(x + 5)(x - 3)$

$5 + (-3) = 2$
$5 \times (-3) = -15$

Confidence bar

Sorted!
☑
☑
☑

Had a look

- You could also factorise this as $5(3xy^2 - x^3y)$ or as $xy(15y - 5x^2)$ but these would not be 'fully factorised, so you would lose a mark.
- Expand the brackets to check your answer.

$5xy(3y - x^2) = 15xy^2 - 5x^3y$

Exam corner

Grade 4

1. Factorise fully
   a) $6x - 2x^2$ b) $14ab + 21a^2$
   c) $xy^2z + xy^2z^2 + xy^2$ **[I got___/6 marks]**

2. Factorise
Grade 5
   a) $x^2 + 9x + 14$ **[___/1 mark]**
   b) $x^2 + 8x - 20$ **[___/2 marks]**
   c) $x^2 - 3x - 18$ **[___/2 marks]**
   d) $x^2 - 10x + 9$ **[___/2 marks]**

Worked example

Grade 5

Factorise fully

a) $15xy^2 - 5x^3y$ **[2 marks]**
b) $x^2 + 7x + 12$ **[2 marks]**
c) $x^2 + 2x - 3$ **[2 marks]**

Solution

a) The HCF of $15xy^2$ and $5x^3y$ is $5xy$, so this goes in front of the brackets. Now work out what goes inside:
   $15xy^2 - 5x^3y = 5xy(3y - x^2)$

b) You need two numbers that multiply to give 12:
   1 and 12   or   2 and 6   or   3 and 4
   Think whether any of these pairs add to give 7:
   $3 + 4 = 7$
   So, $x^2 + 7x + 12 = (x + 3)(x + 4)$

c) You need two numbers that multiply to give –3:
   –1 and 3   or   –3 and 1
   Think whether either of these pairs add to give 2:
   $-1 + 3 = 2$
   So, $x^2 + 2x - 3 = (x - 1)(x + 3)$

CLIMB TO 9 See pages 118–119 for more practice

Factorising 2

You need to know some further techniques for factorising.

Key points

- An expression of the form $a^2 - b^2$ is the **difference of two squares (DOTS)**. You can factorise it as $(a + b)(a - b)$
- Follow these steps to factorise an expression $ax^2 + bx + c$ where a isn't 1, e.g. $2x^2 + 7x + 6$

STEP 1: Work out $a \times c$	$2 \times 6 = 12$
STEP 2: Identify two numbers that multiply to give this value and add to give b	3 and 4, since $3 \times 4 = 12$ and $3 + 4 = 7$
STEP 3: Write the quadratic with the x term split into two x terms using the numbers you found.	$2x^2 + 4x + 3x + 6$
STEP 4: Factorise the pairs of terms.	$2x(x + 2) + 3(x + 2)$
STEP 5: Factorise fully.	$(2x + 3)(x + 2)$

> Always check this type of factorisation by expanding the brackets.

Worked example
Grade 5

Factorise $4x^2 - 9$ **[1 mark]**

Solution

$4x^2$ and 9 are both square terms, so this is DOTS.

The square root of $4x^2$ is $2x$

The square root of 9 is 3

> $(2x)^2 = (2x) \times (2x)$
> $= 4x^2$

So, write these in the brackets, one with + and one with –

$4x^2 - 9 = (2x + 3)(2x - 3)$

Worked example
Grade 7

Factorise fully $12x^2 - x - 1$ **[2 marks]**

Solution

STEP 1: $12 \times -1 = -12$

STEP 2: Numbers are –4 and 3 since $-4 \times 3 = -12$ and $-4 + 3 = -1$

STEP 3: Write as $12x^2 - 4x + 3x - 1$

STEP 4: Factorise: $4x(3x - 1) + 1(3x - 1)$

STEP 5: Factorise fully: $(4x + 1)(3x - 1)$

Exam corner
Grade 5

1. Factorise fully

   a) $x^2 - 8x + 15$ **[I got__/2 marks]**

   b) $24x - 12x^2$ **[__/1 mark]**

   c) $x^2 - 81y^2$ **[__/1 mark]**

2. Factorise
   Grade 7

   a) $5x^2 + 7x + 2$ **[__/2 marks]**

   b) $4x^2 - 21x - 18$ **[__/2 marks]**

   c) $10x^2 - 23x + 12$ **[__/2 marks]**

Checklist for factorising quadratic expressions:

How to factorise a quadractic

- 3 terms, including a factor of x^2: use double brackets. e.g. $x^2 + 6x + 5 = (x + 2)(x + 3)$

- 2 terms and 1 common factor: use single brackets. e.g. $x^2 + 2x = x(x + 3)$

- 2 terms, a minus sign, and they're both square numbers (i.e. DOTS): use two brackets containing square roots. e.g. $x^2 - 16 = (x + 4)(x - 4)$

CLIMB TO 9   See pages 118–119 for more practice

Solving quadratic equations

You need to know how to solve quadratic equations by factorising.

Grade 5–7

Key points

- Quadratic equations are equations that contain an x^2 term. Examples are:

  $x^2 - 4x = 0$ $x^2 + 2x + 1 = 0$ $x^2 - 9 = 0$
- You can sometimes solve quadratic equations to find x by factorising.

Solving quadratic equations by factorising

You are asked to solve a quadratic, e.g. $x^2 + 6x = 7$

↓

Rearrange the equation to get zero on one side:
$x^2 + 6x - 7 = 0$

↓

Factorise into single or double brackets:
$(x + 7)(x - 1) = 0$

↓

Put each factor equal to zero:
$x + 7 = 0$ or $x - 1 = 0$ ⟹ Write the two values of x:
$x = -7$ or $x = 1$

See pages 24 and 25 to recap the different ways of factorising.

Confidence bar

Sorted!

☑
☑
☑

Had a look

Worked example

Grade 5

 Solve $3x^2 + 12x = 0$ **[3 marks]**

Solution

$3x^2 + 12x = 0$ Notice the common factor.

$3x(x + 4) = 0$ Factorise into single brackets.

$3x = 0$ or $x + 4 = 0$ Put each factor equal to zero.

$x = 0$ or $x = -4$

Exam corner

Grade 5

1. Solve

   a) $x^2 + 6x + 8 = 0$ **[I got ___ /3 marks]**

   b) $x^2 - 121 = 0$ **[___ /2 marks]**

   c) $2x^2 - 6x = 0$ **[___ /3 marks]**

   d) $x^2 + x = 12$ **[___ /3 marks]**

2. Solve $5x^2 + 33x - 14 = 0$ **[___ /3 marks]**

Grade 7

Worked example

Grade 7

Solve $6x^2 + 7x - 3 = 0$ **[4 marks]**

Solution

$6 \times -3 = -18$, so find two numbers that multiply to give -18 and add to give 7

The numbers are 9 and -2, since

$9 \times (-2) = -18$ and $9 + (-2) = 7$

Split the x-term into $9x$ and $-2x$

$6x^2 + 7x - 3 = 6x^2 + 9x - 2x - 3$

$= 3x(2x + 3) - (2x + 3)$

$= (3x - 1)(2x + 3)$

The equation becomes:

$(3x - 1)(2x + 3) = 0$

$3x - 1 = 0$ or $2x + 3 = 0$

$x = \dfrac{1}{3}$ or $x = -\dfrac{3}{2}$

Remember to rearrange the equation to get zero on one side.

CLIMB TO **9** See pages 118–119 for more practice

The quadratic formula

Some quadratic equations cannot be solved by factorisation, but this doesn't mean they have no solutions. There is a formula that you can use.

Formula box

To find the solutions of the quadratic equation

$$ax^2 + bx + c = 0$$

use the formula

$$x = \frac{-b \pm \sqrt{b^2 - 4ac}}{2a}$$

Notice the $\pm$ because you will get one solution when you use $+$ and another solution when you use $-$

Remember this...

You need to memorise the quadratic formula. A song or rap can help you. Here is one, sung to either 'Pop goes the weasel' or 'Row, row, row your boat':

" x equals negative b
plus or minus the square root
of b-squared minus 4ac
all over 2a "

Confidence bar

Sorted!

Had a look

Worked example

Grade 7

Solve $x^2 + 7x + 9 = 0$, leaving your answers in surd form. **[3 marks]**

Solution

Start by writing the values of a, b and c: $a = 1$, $b = 7$, $c = 9$

Now substitute into the formula:

$$x = \frac{-7 \pm \sqrt{7^2 - 4 \times 1 \times 9}}{2 \times 1}$$

$$= \frac{-7 \pm \sqrt{13}}{2}$$

The two solutions are

$$x = \frac{-7 + \sqrt{13}}{2} \text{ and } x = \frac{-7 - \sqrt{13}}{2}$$

Worked example

Grade 7

Solve $3x^2 - 5x - 1 = 0$, giving your answers to 3 significant figures. **[3 marks]**

Solution

Write the values of a, b and c: $a = 3$, $b = -5$, $c = -1$

Substitute into the formula, being careful with negative values:

$$x = \frac{-(-5) \pm \sqrt{(-5)^2 - 4 \times 3 \times (-1)}}{2 \times 3}$$

$$= \frac{5 \pm \sqrt{37}}{6}$$

 If you have the square root of a negative number, then you have made an error – go back and check.

Put this in your calculator with the $+$ then with the $-$ to give $x = 1.85$ or $x = -0.180$

Exam corner

1. Solve, giving your answers to 3 significant figures

Grade 7

a) $3x^2 + 8x + 3 = 0$

b) $5x^2 - 8x + 1 = 0$ **[I got ___/6 marks]**

2. Solve $x^2 + 2x - 7 = 0$. Give the value of x in the form $a \pm b\sqrt{2}$, where a and b are constants to be found. **[___/4 marks]**

Grade 8

Examiner's tip!

- If the question tells you to give the solution to a quadratic equation to a certain degree of accuracy, or as a surd, this is a hint to use the quadratic formula.

- Always write the formula with the values substituted in as part of your working.

Completing the square

When you **complete the square** of a quadratic expression, you write it in the form $a(x + b)^2 + c$

Grade 8–9

Key points

- Some quadratic expressions are perfect squares, e.g. $x^2 + 6x + 9$ is $(x + 3)^2$
- The constant in the squared bracket is $\frac{1}{2}$ of the coefficient of x
- If it isn't a perfect square, you can complete the square by working out what needs to be subtracted, e.g. $x^2 + 6x$ is $(x + 3)^2 - 9$

To complete the square of $x^2 + 6x$, split $6x$ into $3x$ and $3x$ ...

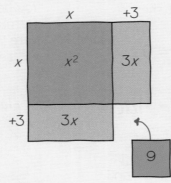

What is missing?
Therefore, $x^2 + 6x$ is $(x + 3)^2 - 9$

Confidence bar

Sorted!

☑
☑
☑

Had a look

Worked example **Grade 8**

a) Complete the square for
$x^2 - 8x + 22$ **[2 marks]**
b) Hence, solve $x^2 - 8x + 22 = 8$ **[3 marks]**

Solution

a) Ignore the constant term for a moment:
$x^2 - 8x = (x - 4)^2 - 16$

$\frac{1}{2}$ of -8 $(-4)^2$

Now, put it all together:
$x^2 - 8x + 22 = (x - 4)^2 - 16 + 22$
$= (x - 4)^2 + 6$

b) Use $(x - 4)^2 + 6 = 8$
$(x - 4)^2 = 2$
$x - 4 = \pm\sqrt{2}$
$x = 4 \pm\sqrt{2}$

Don't forget the negative square root.

Worked example **Grade 9**

Write $3x^2 + 15x + 2$ in the form $a(x + b)^2 + c$, where a, b and c are constants. **[3 marks]**

Solution

Initially ignore the constant term. The coefficient of x^2 is 3, so take out a factor of 3:
$3x^2 + 15x = 3[x^2 + 5]$
Now complete the square inside the square brackets:
$= 3\left[\left(x + \frac{5}{2}\right)^2 - \frac{25}{4}\right]$

$\frac{1}{2}$ of $+5$ $\left(\frac{5}{2}\right)^2$

Expand the square brackets only:
$= 3\left(x + \frac{5}{2}\right)^2 - \frac{75}{4}$
Put it all together:
$3x^2 + 15x + 2 = 3\left(x + \frac{5}{2}\right)^2 - \frac{75}{4} + 2$
$= 3\left(x + \frac{5}{2}\right)^2 - \frac{67}{4}$

Exam corner **Grade 8**

1. a) Complete the square for
i) $x^2 + 14x + 49$ **ii)** $x^2 + 14x$
iii) $x^2 + 14x + 22$ **[I got __/3 marks]**

b) Hence, find the exact solutions to
$x^2 + 14x + 22 = 0$ **[__/3 marks]**

Grade 9

2. Write in the form $p(x + q)^2 + r$
a) $2x^2 + 5x + 10$ **b)** $-x^2 + 4x - 7$
[__/6 marks]

The coefficient of x^2 is -1, so start by taking out a factor of -1

28

Algebraic fractions 1

Fractions involving algebraic terms can be simplified in the same way as numerical fractions.

Key points

You can simplify an algebraic fraction by cancelling **common factors** in the numerator and the denominator.

Cancel all the common factors (algebraic and numerical)

$$\frac{24a}{36a^3} = \frac{\cancel{12} \times 2 \times \cancel{a}}{\cancel{12} \times 3 \times \cancel{a} \times a \times a}$$

$$= \frac{2}{3a^2}$$

$$\frac{(b-1)(b+3)}{2(b-1)^2} = \frac{\cancel{(b-1)}(b+3)}{2\cancel{(b-1)}(b-1)}$$

$$= \frac{(b+3)}{2(b-1)}$$

Confidence bar

Sorted!

☑
☑
☑

Had a look

Worked example

Grade 6

a) Simplify $\dfrac{x^2 + 3x - 10}{x^2 - 25}$ **[3 marks]**

b) Hence, solve $\dfrac{x^2 + 3x - 10}{x^2 - 25} = 2$ **[3 marks]**

Solution

a) First factorise the numerator and the denominator if possible:

$$\frac{x^2 + 3x - 10}{x^2 - 25} = \frac{\cancel{(x+5)}(x-2)}{\cancel{(x+5)}(x-5)}$$ Cancel common factor $(x + 5)$.

$$= \frac{(x-2)}{(x-5)}$$

b) Using part **a**, the equation becomes: $\dfrac{(x-2)}{(x-5)} = 2$

Multiply both sides by $(x - 5)$:

$$x - 2 = 2(x - 5)$$
$$x - 2 = 2x - 10$$
$$x = 8$$

> See pages 24 and 25 for more on factorising, including DOTS which is used here.

> The fraction $\dfrac{(x-2)}{(x-5)}$ will not simplify any further – there are no common factors of the numerator and denominator.
> Be careful, x is not a common factor here, so you can't cancel it.

Exam corner

Grade 6

1. Simplify

a) $\dfrac{15x^3}{18x}$ **[I got __/1 mark]**

b) $\dfrac{6x(x + 2)}{12x^2(x - 2)}$ **[__/2 marks]**

c) $\dfrac{x^2 - 7x}{x^2 - 6x - 7}$ **[__/3 marks]**

d) $\dfrac{2x^2 - x - 1}{x^2 - 1}$ **[__/3 marks]**

2. a) Fully simplify $\dfrac{2x^2 - 9x - 5}{3x^2 - 15x}$ **[__/3 marks]**

Grade 7

b) Hence, solve $\dfrac{2x^2 - 9x - 5}{3x^2 - 15x} = x$ **[__/4 marks]**

> See pages 26 and 27 for solving quadratic equations.

Examiner's tip!

If a question uses the term 'hence', like in Question 2 part b, then you should use the previous part of the question to help you answer it.

This will become a quadratic equation.

Algebraic fractions 2

Fractions involving algebraic terms can be multiplied and divided in the same way as numerical fractions.

Key points

- To multiply algebraic fractions, multiply the numerators and multiply the denominators, then cancel common factors.
- To divide by an algebraic fraction, multiply by its **reciprocal**.

Confidence bar

Sorted!

Had a look

Worked example

Grade 8

Simplify fully

a) $\dfrac{x^2 + 6x}{x^2 + 3x + 2} \times \dfrac{x^2 - 4x - 5}{3x^2}$ **[3 marks]**

b) $\dfrac{5x + 10}{x^2 - 9} \div \dfrac{5x^2}{x + 3}$ **[3 marks]**

Solution

a) First factorise the numerator and denominator of both fractions where possible:

$$\frac{x^2 + 6x}{x^2 + 3x + 2} \times \frac{x^2 - 4x - 5}{3x^2} = \frac{x(x + 6)}{(x + 1)(x + 2)} \times \frac{(x + 1)(x - 5)}{3x^2}$$

$$= \frac{x(x + 6)(x + 1)(x - 5)}{3x^2(x + 1)(x + 2)}$$

$$= \frac{(x + 6)(x - 5)}{3x(x + 2)}$$

> Do not expand brackets when multiplying algebraic fractions.

b) First rewrite as a multiplication, then factorise where possible:

$$\frac{5x + 10}{x^2 - 9} \div \frac{5x^2}{x + 3} = \frac{5x + 10}{x^2 - 9} \times \frac{x + 3}{5x^2}$$

$$= \frac{5(x + 2)}{(x - 3)(x + 3)} \times \frac{x + 3}{5x^2}$$

$$= \frac{5(x + 2)(x + 3)}{5x^2(x - 3)(x + 3)}$$

$$= \frac{x + 2}{x^2(x - 3)}$$

> You can cancel before multiplying if you prefer – but be careful to only cancel common factors of a numerator and a denominator.

See page 6 for a reminder of how to multiply and divide fractions.

Exam corner

Grade 8

1. Simplify fully

   a) $\dfrac{3x}{x + 2} \times \dfrac{2}{3x^2 + 6x}$ [I got ___/3 marks]

   b) $\dfrac{2x^3 - 18x}{x^2 - 2x - 3} \div \dfrac{4x + 12}{x + 1}$ [___/5 marks]

2. Given that $2 : (x^2 + 5) = 1 : 3x$, find the value of x

   [___/4 marks]   **Grade 8**

Examiner's tip!

It is very important that you understand the basic maths concept of ratio. A ratio can appear in exam questions on different topics, such as this algebra question.

Algebraic fractions 3

To add or subtract algebraic fractions, you need a common denominator.

Key points

To add or subtract algebraic fractions...

STEP 1: Factorise the numerators and the denominators wherever possible.

STEP 2: Work out the LCM of the denominators and write the fractions over this common denominator.

STEP 3: Add or subtract the fractions.

STEP 4: Expand brackets in the numerator and simplify.

STEP 5: Simplify further by cancelling common factors if possible.

STEP 1 and STEP 2 here are very important – don't skip them.

If you just 'cross-multiply' by the denominators instead of factorising and using the LCM, the algebra can get quite tricky.

Worked example

Grade 8

Simplify fully $\dfrac{x+1}{x+3} + \dfrac{x-1}{x^2+4x+3}$ **[4 marks]**

See page 5 for a reminder of how to add and subtract fractions.

Solution

$$\frac{x+1}{x+3} + \frac{x-1}{x^2+4x+3} = \frac{x+1}{x+3} + \frac{x-1}{(x+1)(x+3)}$$ ← STEP 1: Factorise where possible.

$$= \frac{(x+1)(x+1)}{(x+1)(x+3)} + \frac{x-1}{(x+1)(x+3)}$$ ← STEP 2: LCM is $(x+1)(x+3)$.

$$= \frac{(x+1)(x+1) + (x-1)}{(x+1)(x+3)}$$ ← STEP 3: Add.

$$= \frac{(x^2+2x+1) + (x-1)}{(x+1)(x+3)}$$ ← STEP 4: Expand brackets in numerator and simplify.

$$= \frac{x^2+3x}{(x+1)(x+3)}$$

$$= \frac{x(x+3)}{(x+1)(x+3)}$$ ← STEP 5: Cancel common factors.

$$= \frac{x}{x+1}$$

Remember to multiply the numerator of the first fraction by $(x+1)$.

Exam corner

Grade 7

1. Simplify fully

a) $\dfrac{x}{2} + \dfrac{x}{5}$ **[I got __/2 marks]**

b) $\dfrac{x+2}{2} - \dfrac{x-1}{4}$ **[__/3 marks]**

c) $\dfrac{1}{x+5} + \dfrac{2}{x-3}$ **[__/3 marks]**

d) $\dfrac{2}{x+1} - \dfrac{1}{2x-1}$ **[__/3 marks]**

Grade 9

2. a) Show that $\dfrac{1}{3x-1} - \dfrac{2}{9x^2-1} \equiv \dfrac{1}{ax+b}$
where a and b are constants to be found.
[__/4 marks]

b) Hence, solve $\dfrac{1}{3x-1} - \dfrac{2}{9x^2-1} = 1-x$
[__/4 marks]

Rearranging formulae

A formula can be rearranged to make a different letter the **subject**. The subject of an equation is a variable that sits by itself on either the left or right-hand side of the equals sign.

Key points

Rearranging a formula is very similar to solving an equation.

You can use the **balance method** to get the letter you want as the **subject** on its own.

 See page 16 for more on the balance method.

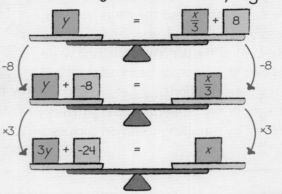

To make x the subject of the formula $y = \frac{x}{3} + 8$

The answer is $x = 3y - 24$

Worked example

Rearrange $y = 2\sqrt{x} - 5$ to make x the subject. **[3 marks]**

Solution

$y + 5 = 2\sqrt{x} - 5 + 5$ Add 5 to both sides.

$y + 5 = 2\sqrt{x}$

$\dfrac{y + 5}{2} = \dfrac{2\sqrt{x}}{2}$ Divide both sides by 2

$\dfrac{y + 5}{2} = \sqrt{x}$

$\left(\dfrac{y + 5}{2}\right)^2 = (\sqrt{x})^2$ Square both sides.

$\left(\dfrac{y + 5}{2}\right)^2 = x$ You can re-write as...

$x = \left(\dfrac{y + 5}{2}\right)^2$

Worked example

Rearrange $\dfrac{1}{a} = \dfrac{1}{b} + \dfrac{1}{c}$ to make b the subject. **[3 marks]**

Solution

$\dfrac{1}{a} \times abc = \dfrac{1}{b} \times abc + \dfrac{1}{c} \times abc$ Multiply every term by the denominators.

$bc = ac + ab$

$bc - ab = ac + ab - ab$ Subtract ab so all terms involving b are on the same side of the equation.

$bc - ab = ac$

$b(c - a) = ac$ Factorise.

$\dfrac{b(c - a)}{c - a} = \dfrac{ac}{c - a}$ Divide by $(c - a)$.

$b = \dfrac{ac}{c - a}$

Exam corner

1. You are given the formula $E = \frac{1}{2}ms^2$

   s represents the speed of a particle.

   a) Rearrange the formula to make s the subject.

   [I got ___/3 marks]

   b) Work out the speed of the particle when $E = 8$ and $m = 4$

   [___/2 marks]

2. Make x the subject of $x + 2 = \dfrac{5 - x}{y}$ **[___/3 marks]**

Examiner's tip!

Check your answer by substituting it into the original formula.

Here, substitute your answer for s, along with $m = 4$. If you get $E = 8$ then your value is correct.

CLIMB TO 9 See pages 118–119 for more practice

Quadratic graphs 1

You need to be able to draw and interpret quadratic graphs.

Grade

4–5

Key points

- A **quadratic** graph has equation
  $$y = ax^2 + bx + c$$
  where a, b and c are numbers.
- The x-intercepts give the **roots** (the solutions) of
  $$ax^2 + bx + c = 0$$
- The turning point of the graph is the maximum or minimum.

Quadratic graphs:

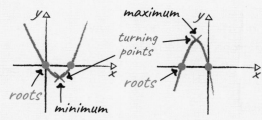

X marks the turning points

Confidence bar

Sorted!

☑
☑
☑

Had a look

Worked example

Grade **5**

Here is the graph of $y = x^2 + 2x - 1$

a) Write the coordinates of the turning point of
   $y = x^2 + 2x - 1$ **[1 mark]**

b) Write estimates for the roots of
   $x^2 + 2x - 1 = 0$ **[2 marks]**

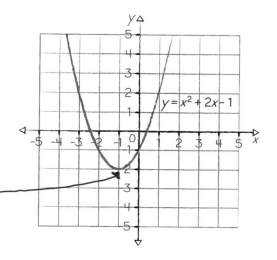

Solution

a) The turning point is the minimum point, which has coordinates (–1, –2).

b) The roots of $x^2 + 2x - 1 = 0$ are the x-intercepts of the graph.
   Approximately, $x = -2.4$ and $x = 0.4$

Exam corner

Grade **4**

1. a) Complete the table of values for the equation
      $y = 2x^2 - 4$ **[I got ___/2 marks]**

x	–2	–1	0	1	2
y	4	–2	–4	–2	4

   b) Draw the graph of $y = 2x^2 - 4$ **[___/2 marks]**

2. Here is the graph of $y = -x^2 - 4x - 1$

   a) Write the coordinates of the turning point
      of $y = -x^2 - 4x - 1$ **[___/1 mark]**

   b) Write estimates for the roots of
      $-x^2 - 4x - 1 = 0$ **[___/2 marks]**

Grade **5**

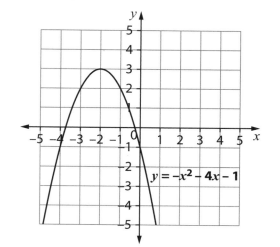

Quadratic graphs 2

You don't always need an accurate drawing of a graph - often you can just make a sketch.

Key points

- A **sketch** of a quadratic graph should show the shape of the graph and some key information:
  - the y-intercept
  - the x-intercept(s)
  - the turning point if asked for.
- You can use the sketch of $y = f(x)$ to work out whether $f(x)$ has **real roots**, i.e. real number solutions to the equation $f(x) = 0$
- You can complete the square to find the coordinates of the **turning point**. If the graph has equation
$y = a(x - b)^2 + c,$
then the turning point is (b, c).

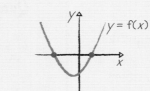

2 x-intercepts, so $f(x)$ has 2 real roots.

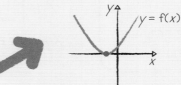

1 x-intercept, so $f(x)$ has 1 real root.

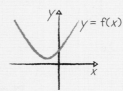

0 x-intercepts, so $f(x)$ has 0 real roots.

See page 33 for more on roots and turning points.

Confidence bar

Sorted!

☑
☑
☑

Had a look

Worked example

Grade **8**

Work out the coordinates of the turning point of the graph of $y = 2x^2 + 8x + 1$ **[4 marks]**

Solution

$2x^2 + 8x = 2[x^2 + 4]$
$\qquad\quad = 2[(x + 2)^2 - 4]$
$2x^2 + 8x + 1 = 2(x + 2)^2 - 8 + 1$
$\qquad\qquad\quad = 2(x + 2)^2 - 7$
Turning point is at $(-2, -7)$.

See page 28 for a reminder on how to complete the square.

Careful with the sign for the x-coordinate.

Worked example

Grade **7**

Draw the graph of $y = (5 - x)(5 + x)$. **[3 marks]**

Solution

When $x = 0$, $y = 25$, so y-intercept is 25
When $y = 0$, $x = 5$ or -5,
so x-intercepts are 5 and -5
The coefficient of x^2 in the equation is negative, so the graph looks like this.

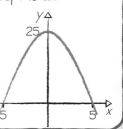

Exam corner

Grade **7**

1. Draw these graphs.

   a) $y = x(x + 2)$ **[I got ___/2 marks]**

   b) $y = (x - 4)^2$ **[___/3 marks]**

   c) $y = -(x + 1)(x - 2)$ **[___/3 marks]**

   d) $(5 - x)(x + 5)$ **[___/3 marks]**

Grade **9**

2. $f(x) = x^2 + x + 1$

   a) Work out the coordinates of the turning point of the graph of $y = f(x)$.
   [___/4 marks]

   b) Hence, draw the graph of $y = f(x)$.
   [___/3 marks]

   c) Does $f(x)$ has any real roots? Give a reason for your answer. **[___/2 marks]**

Quadratic inequalities

You can use sketches of quadratic graphs to help solve quadratic inequalities.

Key points

- You can sometimes use the balance method to solve quadratic inequalities. Then, for the final step:
  $x^2 < a^2 \Rightarrow -a < x < a$
  $x^2 > a^2 \Rightarrow x < -a$ or $x > a$
- To solve trickier quadratic inequalities:

STEP 1: Treat the inequality as an equation of the form $f(x) = 0$ and solve.

STEP 2: Draw the graph of $y = f(x)$.

STEP 3: Write the solution using inequality notation.

Worked example
Grade 8

Solve $3x^2 - 2 > 13$ **[3 marks]**

Solution

$3x^2 - 2 > 13 \Rightarrow 3x^2 > 15 \Rightarrow x^2 > 5$

So, $x < -\sqrt{5}$ or $x > \sqrt{5}$

Confidence bar

Sorted!

Had a look

Take care writing inequalities...

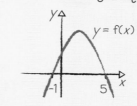

$f(x) < 0$ is two separate sections of curve, so you need two separate inequalities: $x < -1$ or $x > 5$

$f(x) > 0$ is a single section of curve, so you can combine inequalities: $-1 < x < 5$

Worked example
Grade 9

 Solve $2x^2 - 5x \leq 12$, giving your answer in set notation.   **[4 marks]**

Solution

First rearrange to: $2x^2 - 5x - 12 \leq 0$

STEP 1: $2x^2 - 5x - 12 = 0$

$2x^2 - 8x + 3x - 12 = 0$ since $(-8) \times 3 = -24$
                                    and $(-8) + 3 = -5$

$2x(x - 4) + 3(x - 4) = 0$

$(2x + 3)(x - 4) = 0$

$2x + 3 = 0$ or $x - 4 = 0$

$x = -\frac{3}{2}$ or $x = 4$

See page 26 for solving this type of quadratic equation.

STEP 2:

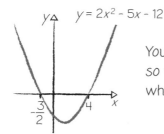
$y = 2x^2 - 5x - 12$

You are solving $2x^2 - 5x - 12 \leq 0$, so you need the part of the graph where $y \leq 0$

STEP 3: You want the single section of curve between $-\frac{3}{2}$ and 4

Therefore, $-\frac{3}{2} \leq x \leq 4$

In set notation $\left\{ x : -\frac{3}{2} \leq x \leq 4 \right\}$

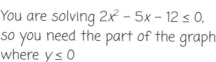
Make sure you use the correct inequality symbol for the question (here $\leq$ not $<$).

See page 20 for more on solving inequalities.

Exam corner

Grade 8

 1. Solve

    a) $x^2 < 9$
                 [I got __/1 mark]

    b) $5x^2 > 80$
                     [__/2 marks]

    c) $4x^2 + 7 \leq 15$
                     [__/3 marks]

Grade 9

2. Solve, giving your answers in set notation

    a) $x^2 - 7x + 10 < 0$
                     [__/4 marks]

    b) $3x^2 - 2x \geq 1$
                     [__/4 marks]

    c) $x^2 + 4x + 1 \leq 0$
                     [__/4 marks]

Non-linear simultaneous equations

You can solve simultaneous equations where one is non-linear using the **substitution method**.

Key points

Substitution method for simultaneous equations:

STEP 1: Rearrange the linear equation to make x (or y) the subject.

STEP 2: Substitute for x (or y) in the non-linear equation.

STEP 3: Solve this quadratic equation to find two solutions for y (or x).

STEP 4: Substitute each of these solutions back into the original linear equation to find corresponding solutions for x (or y).

Worked example

Grade 8

Solve the simultaneous equations.
$2x + y = 10 \qquad x^2 + y^2 = 40$
Show all your working. **[4 marks]**

Solution

STEP 1: $y = 10 - 2x$

STEP 2: $x^2 + (10 - 2x)^2 = 40$

STEP 3: $x^2 + 100 - 40x + 4x^2 = 40$

$5x^2 - 40x + 60 = 0$

$x^2 - 8x + 12 = 0$

$(x - 2)(x - 6) = 0$

$x = 2$ or $x = 6$

STEP 4: When $x = 2$, $y = 10 - 2(2) = 6$

When $x = 6$, $y = 10 - 2(6) = -2$

> It's a bit easier to substitute for y here, but it doesn't matter if you choose x – you should get the same final solution.

This solution tells you that the graphs of $2x + y = 10$ and $x^2 + y^2 = 40$ intersect at the points $(2, 6)$ and $(6, -2)$.

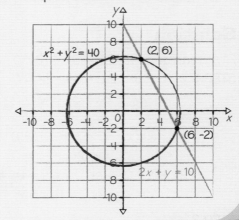

> Double check your solutions for x and y by substituting them into the other equation and checking it balances.

Exam corner

Grade 8

1. Use algebra to solve each pair of simultaneous equations.

   a) $x + y = 6$, $x^2 - y^2 = 144$ **[I got ___/4 marks]**

   b) $y = x + 2$, $x + y^2 = 0$ **[___/4 marks]**

   c) $2x + y = 19$, $x^2 - xy = 14$ **[___/4 marks]**

2. A circle, C, is centred at the origin and has radius $\sqrt{5}$
   A tangent to C at the point A has equation $x - 2y + 5 = 0$
   Work out the coordinates of A **[___/6 marks]**

   Grade 9

Examiner's tip!

CLIMB TO 9

If you are told to use algebra, then it means you must show your full working – you shouldn't just guess and substitute in values.

📄 See page 40 for the equation of a circle.

CLIMB TO 9 See pages 118–119 for more practice

Solutions from graphs

You can use graphs to find approximate solutions to simultaneous equations.

Key points

The solution to a pair of simultaneous equations is the point of intersection of their graphs.

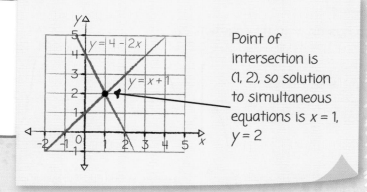

Point of intersection is (1, 2), so solution to simultaneous equations is $x = 1$, $y = 2$

Worked example

Grade **7**

Use a graphical method to estimate, to 1 decimal place, the solutions to the simultaneous equations $y = x^2 - 2x$ and $y = x + 1$ **[4 marks]**

Solution

First draw a table of values for the quadratic graph, $y = x^2 - 2x$:

x	-1	0	1	2	3
y	3	0	-1	0	3

$y = x + 1$ is a straight line with gradient 1 and y-intercept 1

Plot the two graphs.

The solutions are approximately $x = -0.3$, $y = 0.7$ and $x = 3.3$, $y = 4.3$

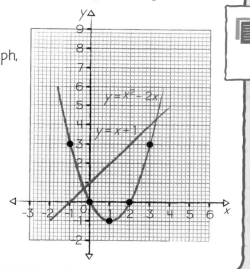

See pages 17 and 18 for linear graphs.

Exam corner

Grade **7**

1. The graph of $x^2 + y^2 = 4$ is given. Use a graphical method to solve the simultaneous equations $x^2 + y^2 = 4$ and $y = 1 - \frac{1}{2}x$ **[I got ___/3 marks]**

2. The graph of $y = x^3 + x^2 + x$ is given. Use the graph to estimate the solution to the equation $x^3 + x^2 + 3x = 1$ **[___/3 marks]**

Start by rearranging the second equation to get $x^3 + x^2 + x$ on one side. What's now on the other side? Try drawing this on the graph.

Grade **8**

Cubic and reciprocal graphs

You need to be able to draw and recognise cubic and reciprocal graphs.

Key points

● A **cubic graph** has an x^3 in its equation, e.g.

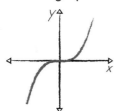
$y = x^3$

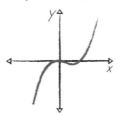
$y = x^3 - x^2$

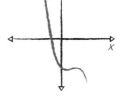
$y = -x^3 + 2x^2 - x - 2$

● A **reciprocal graph** has x in the denominator, e.g.

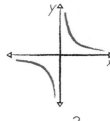
$y = \dfrac{2}{x}$
$y = -\dfrac{1}{x}$

> When $y = \dfrac{1}{x}$, the value of x cannot be 0, because $\dfrac{1}{0}$ is not a defined value. The curve will get closer and closer to the axes but will never touch them.

Worked example

a) Complete the table of values for $y = x^3 + x^2 - 4x - 4$ **[2 marks]**
b) Draw the graph of $y = x^3 + x^2 - 4x - 4$ **[2 marks]**
c) Use your graph to write the solutions to the equation $x^3 + x^2 - 4x - 4 = 0$ **[2 marks]**

Solution

x	-3	-2	-1	0	1	2	3
y	-10	0	0	-4	-6	0	20

When $x = -1$,
$y = (-1)^3 + (-1)^2 - 4(-1) - 4 = 0$
When $x = 0$, $y = -4$
When $x = 2$, $y = 2^3 + 2^2 - 4(2) - 4 = 0$
When $x = 3$, $y = 3^3 + 3^2 - 4(3) - 4 = 20$
b) Plot these points and join up to form a smooth curve.

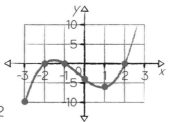

c) The solutions are the x-intercepts, so $x = -2, -1, 2$

> Start with what you know about this graph: it's a reciprocal graph in the form $y = -\dfrac{a}{x}$. Use the coordinate given to work out a.

Exam corner

1. a) Complete the table of values for $y = 2x^3$
[I got___/2 marks]

x	-2	-1	0	1	2
y				2	

b) Draw the graph of $y = 2x^3$ **[___/2 marks]**

2. Work out the equation for this graph.
[___/2 marks]

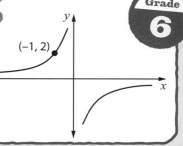
$(-1, 2)$

Exponential graphs

Functions where the variable is in the power are called **exponential** functions. An example is $y = 2^x$

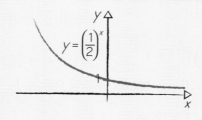

$k > 1$ indicates exponential growth

$k < 1$ indicates exponential decay

Worked example

Grade 7

The number, N, of bacteria in a Petri dish at the start of an experiment is 300. The number of bacteria in the dish after t hours is given by $N = A \times 1.05^t$, where A is a constant.

a) Work out the value of A **[2 marks]**

b) How many bacteria will be in the dish after 7 hours? **[2 marks]**

c) Draw the graph of N against t **[2 marks]**

Solution

a) Initially, $t = 0$ and $N = 300$

Substitute into the equation:

$A \times 1.05^0 = 300$

$A = 300$ since $1.05^0 = 1$

b) Number of bacteria $= 300 \times 1.05^7 = 422$

c)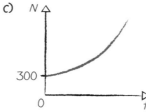

Key points

- An exponential function is of the form $y = k^x$ where k is a positive constant.
- The graph of $y = k^x$ has y-intercept 1 (since $k^0 = 1$ for any k).
- The graph of $y = Ak^x$ will have y-intercept A

Exam corner

Grade 6

1. a) Circle the equation of each graph.

   i) $y = \dfrac{2}{x}$ $y = 2x^3$ $y = -\dfrac{2}{x}$ $y = 2^x$ ii) $y = \dfrac{2}{x}$ $y = 2x^3$ $y = -\dfrac{2}{x}$ $y = 2^x$ **[I got__/2 marks]**

   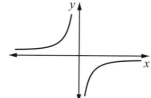   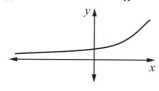

   Grade 7

   b) Draw the graph of $y = 2 \times 3^x$ **[__/2 marks]**

2. The value, £V, of a used car is given by $V = A \times 0.9^t$ where t is the age of the car in years and A is a positive constant. After three years, the value of the car is £4370

   a) Work out the percentage decrease in the value of the car each year. **[__/1 mark]**

   b) Work out the value of A to 3 significant figures. **[__/2 marks]**

See page 60 for more on growth and depreciation (decay).

Equation of a circle

A circle is the set of points that are a fixed distance (the radius) from a point. You need to know the equation of a circle with centre the origin.

Key points

$$x^2 + y^2 = r^2$$

- This is the equation of a circle with centre $(0, 0)$ and radius r

- To find the equation $y = mx + c$ of a tangent to a circle at a point:

  STEP 1: Work out the gradient of the radius at the point.

  STEP 2: Use the fact that the tangent is perpendicular to the radius to find m (i.e. use negative reciprocal).

  STEP 3: Substitute m and the coordinates of the point into $y = mx + c$ to find c

  STEP 4: Write out the equation using the values of m and c found.

Pythagoras' theorem shows where the circle equation comes from:

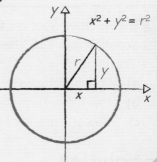

Worked example
Grade 8

a) Write the equation of the circle shown. **[1 mark]**

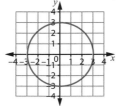

b) Show that the point $(-1, 2\sqrt{2})$ lies on the circle. **[2 marks]**

Solution

a) The centre of the circle is the origin and its radius is 3, so its equation is $x^2 + y^2 = 9$

b) Substitute coordinates into left-hand side of equation:
$$x^2 + y^2 = (-1)^2 + (2\sqrt{2})^2$$
$$= 1 + 8 = 9 \checkmark$$
So, the point lies on the circle.

See page 19 for perpendicular lines and page 69 for tangents to circles.

Worked example
Grade 9

A circle has equation $x^2 + y^2 = 100$
The point $A(6, -8)$ lies on the circle.
Work out the equation of the tangent to the circle at A **[5 marks]**

Solution

STEP 1: Gradient of radius $OA = \dfrac{-8}{6} = -\dfrac{4}{3}$

STEP 2: Gradient of tangent at $A = \dfrac{3}{4}$

STEP 3: Substitute $x = 6$, $y = -8$ into $y = \dfrac{3}{4}x + c$:
$$-8 = \dfrac{3}{4}(6) + c$$
$$-8 = \dfrac{9}{2} + c \Rightarrow c = -\dfrac{25}{2}$$

STEP 4: Equation is $y = \dfrac{3}{4}x - \dfrac{25}{2}$

Exam corner
Grade 8　　**Grade 9**

1. A circle has equation $x^2 + y^2 = 18$

  a) Work out the radius of the circle. **[I got __/1 mark]**

  The point $(a, 4)$ lies on the circle.

  b) Work out the possible values of a **[__/2 marks]**

2. Work out the equation of the tangent to the circle $x^2 + y^2 = 30$ at the point $(-5, -\sqrt{5})$. **[__/5 marks]**

Trigonometric graphs

You need to be able to draw the graphs of the trigonometric functions
$y = \sin x$, $y = \cos x$ and $y = \tan x$

Key points

Learn the shapes and key features of these graphs.

$y = \sin x$

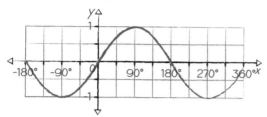

$y = \cos x$

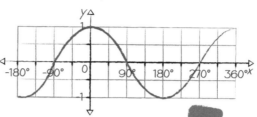

The maximum value of $\sin x$ and of $\cos x$ is 1 and the minimum is –1
The graphs of $y = \sin x$ and $y = \cos x$ both repeat every 360°

$y = \tan x$

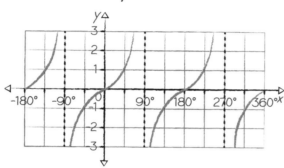

Remember the difference between the sine and cosine graphs.
Between 0 and 360°...

sine is like a wave

cosine is like a bucket

There is no maximum or minimum value of $\tan x$
It can be any value but is undefined at $x = \pm 90°, \pm 270°, ...$
The graph of $y = \tan x$ repeats every 180°

 See page 86 for exact values of trigonometric functions.

Exam corner

a) Draw the graph of $y = \tan x$ for
$0° \leq x \leq 360°$ **[I got ___/2 marks]**

b) Given that $\tan 60° = \sqrt{3}$, write
another angle, θ, such that
$\tan \theta = \sqrt{3}$ **[___/1 mark]**

c) Use your graph to solve the
equation $\tan x = -\tan 100°$ for
$0 \leq x < 180°$ **[___/1 mark]**

Worked example

a) Write the value of $\sin 60°$ **[1 mark]**

b) Use the graph of $y = \sin x$ to work out the value of
i) $\sin 120°$ **ii)** $\sin 300°$ **[3 marks]**

Solution

a) $\sin 60° = \dfrac{\sqrt{3}}{2}$

b) Draw the graph
between 0° and 360°

i) From the graph
you can see that
$\sin 120° = \sin 60°$
$= \dfrac{\sqrt{3}}{2}$

ii) Also, $\sin 300° = -\sin 60° = -\dfrac{\sqrt{3}}{2}$

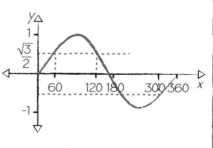

Graph transformations 1

You can transform a graph by translating it either horizontally or vertically.

Key points

If you have the graph of $y = f(x)$, then

● $y = f(x + a)$ is a **translation** of a units **left**
● $y = f(x) + a$ is a translation of a units **up**

Remember this...

For $y = f(x)$...

The x is inside the brackets, so $f(x + a)$ will change the x-coordinate.

The y is outside the brackets, so $f(x) + a$ will change the y-coordinate.

Confidence bar

Sorted!

☑
☑
☑

Had a look

Worked example
Grade 8

The graph of $y = f(x)$ is shown. Draw the graph of $y = f(x - 2)$. **[2 marks]**

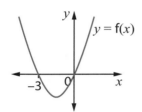

Solution

The graph is translated 2 units to the <u>right</u>. Add 2 onto the x-intercepts.

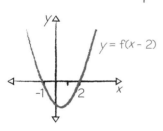

Worked example
Grade 8

a) Draw the graph of $y = 1 + \cos x$ for $-180° \le x \le 180°$. Label any points where the graph intersects the x-axis or the y-axis. **[3 marks]**

b) State the coordinates of the maximum point on the curve in the range $-180° \le x \le 180°$. **[2 marks]**

Solution

a) This will be the same as the graph of $y = \cos x$ but translated up 1 unit.

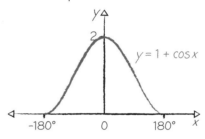

b) The maximum point on $y = \cos x$ in the range $-180° \le x \le 180°$ has coordinates $(0, 1)$. Therefore, the maximum point on this curve is $(0, 2)$.

Exam corner
Grade 8

1. A graph with equation $y = f(x)$ has a minimum point at $(1, -2)$. Give the coordinates of the minimum point of the graph with equation

   a) $y = f(x + 1)$ **[I got ___/1 mark]**   b) $y = f(x - 2) - 3$ **[___/2 marks]**

2. The graph of $y = f(x)$ is shown. Draw the graph of $y = f(x - 1)$. Label the x-intercepts. **[___ /2 marks]**
Grade 8

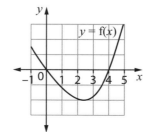

Remember, if you have +1 inside the brackets then you must <u>subtract</u> 1 from the x-coordinates.

Graph transformations 2

You can transform a graph by reflecting it in the *x*-axis or the *y*-axis.

Key points

If you have the graph of $y = f(x)$, then
- $y = -f(x)$ is a **reflection** in the *x*-axis
- $y = f(-x)$ is a **reflection** in the *y*-axis.

Remember this...

For $y = f(x)$...

The *x* is inside the brackets, so $f(-x)$ will change the *x*-coordinate.

The *y* is outside the brackets, so $-f(x)$ will change the *y*-coordinate.

Worked example

Grade 8

The graph of $y = f(x)$ is shown.

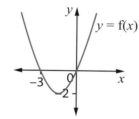

Draw the graph of $y = -f(x)$. **[2 marks]**

Solution

The graph is reflected in the *x*-axis. The *x*-intercepts stay the same, as it's the *y*-coordinates that are affected.

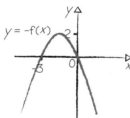

Worked example

Grade 8

A graph with equation $y = f(x)$ has a turning point at (3, 5).
Give the coordinates of the turning point of the graph with equation $y = -f(x + 5)$. **[2 marks]**

Solution

The 5 inside the brackets tells you to subtract 5 from the *x*-coordinate.

The negative sign outside the brackets tells you to multiply the *y*-coordinate by -1

Therefore, the turning point of $y = -f(x + 5)$ is (-2, -5).

Exam corner

Grade 8

1. A graph with equation $y = f(x)$ has a minimum point at (1, −2).
   Give the coordinates of the turning point of the graph with equation

   a) $y = -f(x)$ **b)** $y = f(-x)$ **[I got ___/2 marks]**

2. The graph of $y = f(x)$ is shown.
   Draw the graph of $y = f(-x) + 2$
   Label the *x*-intercepts. **[___ /3 marks]**

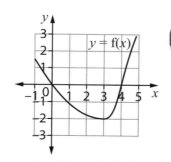

Grade 8

Note that Question 2 involves a translation as well as a reflection.

Simple kinematic graphs

You need to be able to draw and interpret graphs involving distance, time and speed.

Key points

On a distance-time graph,
● the gradient is the speed.
On a speed-time (or velocity-time) graph,
● the gradient is the acceleration
● the area under the graph is the distance.

'Velocity' is speed in a particular direction.

Interpreting the gradient...

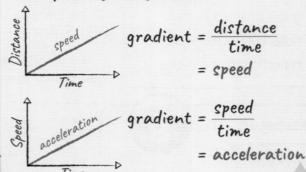

$$\text{gradient} = \frac{\text{distance}}{\text{time}} = \text{speed}$$

$$\text{gradient} = \frac{\text{speed}}{\text{time}} = \text{acceleration}$$

Worked example

Sophie drives a total of 14 km to work.
● She travels the first 6 km at a constant speed of 36 km/h.
● She then stops for 5 minutes at roadworks.
● It takes her 15 minutes to complete the rest of the journey at a constant speed.

Draw a distance–time graph of the journey.
[4 marks]

Solution

Work out time taken to travel first 6 km, using the formula: time = distance ÷ speed.

$$\text{Time} = 6 \div 36 = \tfrac{1}{6} \text{ hour} = 10 \text{ minutes}$$

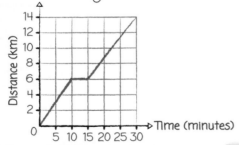

Worked example

The speed–time graph shows the motion of a particle.

a) Describe the motion of the particle. **[3 marks]**

b) Work out the acceleration in the first 4 seconds. **[2 marks]**

c) Work out the total distance travelled. **[3 marks]**

Solution

a) The particle accelerates from rest for 4 s, then travels at a constant speed of 10 m/s for 6 s, then decelerates for 2 s to become stationary.

b) Gradient of line $= \dfrac{10}{4} = 2.5$
Acceleration = 2.5 m/s²

 See page 74 for the formula for the area of a trapezium.

c) Area of trapezium under graph $= \tfrac{1}{2}(12 + 6) \times 10 = 90$
Distance = 90 m

In part **b**, you are told the distance travelled and you know this is equal to the area under the graph. To find T, try rearranging the formula for the area of a triangle.

Exam corner

The graph shows the speed of an object over a period of T seconds. After 2 s, the object is travelling at 12 m/s.

a) Work out the acceleration in the first 2 seconds.
[I got ___/2 marks]

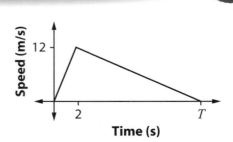

The object travels a total of 108 m during T seconds.

b) Work out the value of T **[___/2 marks]**

Estimating areas

You can estimate the area under a curve using trapeziums.

Key points

To estimate the area under a curve:

STEP 1: Draw vertical lines to split the curve into a number of strips.

STEP 2: Draw a chord to approximate the curve in each strip.

STEP 3: Work out the area of each of the trapeziums (or rectangles or triangles).

STEP 4: Add up to find an estimate for the total area.

Your answer could either be

an underestimate   or   an overestimate

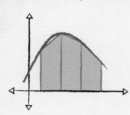 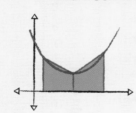

of the actual area

Worked example

Grade 8

Here is the velocity–time graph for an object.

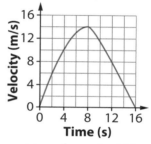

a) Use three strips of equal width to estimate the distance travelled by the object in the first 12 s. **[3 marks]**

b) Is your answer to part **a** an overestimate or an underestimate of the actual distance? Give a reason for your answer. **[1 mark]**

Solution

a) STEP 1: Draw vertical lines at 4, 8 and 12 s to create three strips.
STEP 2: Draw a chord in each of the strips.
STEP 3: Work out each area:

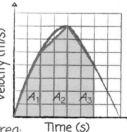

$$A_1 = \frac{1}{2} \times (10 + 0) \times 4 = 20$$
$$A_2 = \frac{1}{2} \times (10 + 14) \times 4 = 48$$ (trapezia)
$$A_3 = \frac{1}{2} \times (14 + 8) \times 4 = 44$$

STEP 4: Add: $20 + 48 + 44 = 112$
Distance travelled ≈ 112 m

b) It is an underestimate since all the chords lie under the curve.

Exam corner

Grade 8

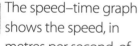The speed–time graph shows the speed, in metres per second, of an object t seconds after it starts to move.

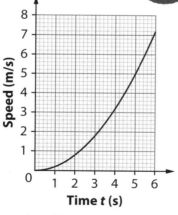

a) Use three strips of equal width to estimate the area under the graph between $t = 2$ s and $t = 5$ s. **[I got ___/3 marks]**

b) Describe fully what your answer to part **a** represents. **[___/2 marks]**

c) Does your answer in part **a** give an underestimate or an overestimate for the area under the graph? Give a reason for your answer. **[___/1 mark]**

Rates of change

The gradient of a graph can show how a value changes over time.

Key points

- A positive gradient means the value is increasing.
- A negative gradient means the value is decreasing.
- The steeper the graph, the faster the value is changing.

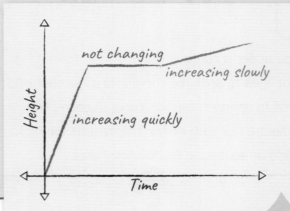

Worked example

The graph shows the height of a chilli plant at the end of each week.

a) How tall was the plant after 3 weeks? **[1 mark]**
b) In which week did the plant not grow? **[1 mark]**
c) When did the plant grow the fastest and what was its speed of growth during this time? **[2 marks]**

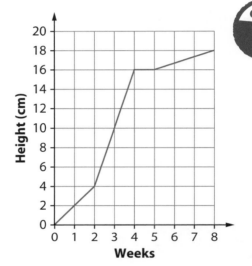

Grade
4

Solution

a) It was 10 cm tall.

b) It didn't grow during the 5th week.

c) The fastest increase was between 2 and 4 weeks.
The speed of growth was $\frac{12}{2}$ = 6 cm/week.

Exam corner

1. This graph shows the cost of hiring a cement mixer.

   The total cost is given by the formula:

   total cost = fixed fee + cost per day × number of days

   Use the graph to work out

   a) the fixed fee **[I got ___/1 mark]**

   b) the cost per day. **[___/2 marks]**

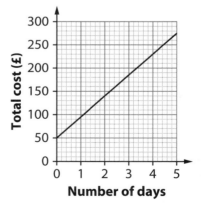

Grade
4

2. These vases are filled with water at a constant rate. Draw a graph for each to show how the depth of water varies over time. **[___/3 marks]**

   a) b) c)

Grade
5

Gradients of curves

You can use a chord to work out the average gradient of a curve between two points. Or you can use a tangent to estimate the gradient at a point.

Grade 8

Key points

- To work out the average gradient between two points, draw a chord connecting the two points and work out the gradient of the chord.
- To estimate the **gradient at a point**, draw a **tangent** to the curve at that point and work out the gradient of the tangent.

 See page 44 for more on what gradients represent.

Worked example

Grade 8

The distance–time graph for a train on part of a journey is shown.

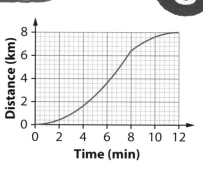

a) Work out the train's average speed in km/h during the first 4 minutes. **[3 marks]**

b) Estimate the train's speed after 10 minutes. **[2 marks]**

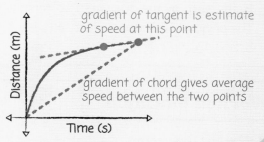

For a distance-time graph...

gradient of tangent is estimate of speed at this point

gradient of chord gives average speed between the two points

Solution

a) Draw a chord connecting the points on the curve where $x = 0$ and $x = 2$

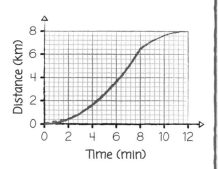

Gradient of chord $= \dfrac{\text{change in } y}{\text{change in } x} = \dfrac{0.4}{2} = 0.2$

Average speed $= 0.2\,\text{km/min} = 12\,\text{km/h}$

b) Draw a tangent to the graph at $x = 10$ and a triangle to work out the gradient.

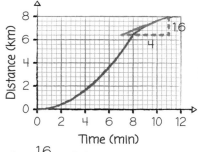

Gradient of tangent $= \dfrac{1.6}{4} = 0.4$

Speed $\approx 0.4\,\text{km/min} = 24\,\text{km/h}$

Exam corner

Grade 8

The graph shows the velocity of a ball t seconds after being dropped out of a window.

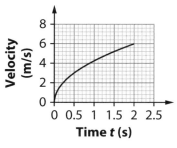

Work out the average acceleration of the ball during these 2 seconds. **[I got ___/2 marks]**

Remember, a tangent to a curve at a point has the same gradient as the curve at that point.

Types of sequence

You need to be able to recognise different types of sequence and use term-to-term and position-to-term rules.

Key points

- A number in a sequence is called a **term**.
- A **term-to-term rule** tells you how to work out each term in the sequence from the term before.
- The **nth term** of a sequence is a rule that gives all the terms of a sequence when you substitute values for n
- In an **arithmetic sequence**, you add or subtract a number to get the next term.
- In a **geometric sequence**, you multiply or divide by a number to get the next term.
- In a **Fibonacci-type sequence**, each term is the sum of the previous two terms. The original Fibonacci sequence is 1, 1, 2, 3, 5, 8, 13, 21, …

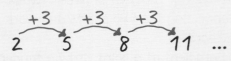

Arithmetic sequence: Add or subtract each time

$$\underset{2}{} \xrightarrow{+3} \underset{5}{} \xrightarrow{+3} \underset{8}{} \xrightarrow{+3} \underset{11}{} \dots$$

Geometric sequence: Multiply or divide each time

$$\underset{2}{} \xrightarrow{\times 3} \underset{6}{} \xrightarrow{\times 3} \underset{18}{} \xrightarrow{\times 3} \underset{54}{} \dots$$

Worked example · Grade 6

a) The first three terms of a Fibonacci-type sequence are: $k, k + 6, 2k + 6$
   Work out the 4th term of the sequence. **[3 marks]**

b) A different sequence has nth term rule $(\sqrt{5})^n$
   i) Work out the 4th term of the sequence. **[1 mark]**
   ii) Write the type of sequence and the term-to-term rule. **[2 marks]**

Solution

a) 4th term = 2nd term + 3rd term
      $= (k + 6) + (2k + 6) = 3k + 12$

b) i) 4th term $= (\sqrt{5})^4 = (5^{\frac{1}{2}})^4 = 5^2 = 25$

   ii) A geometric sequence with term-to-term rule 'multiply by $\sqrt{5}$'

Worked example · Grade 4

The nth term of a sequence is $11 + 3n$

a) Work out the 7th term of the sequence. **[1 mark]**

b) Is 81 a term of this sequence? Show how you get your answer. **[2 marks]**

Solution

a) To find the 7th term, substitute $n = 7$:
   7th term $= 11 + 3 \times 7 = 32$

b) Consider the equation $11 + 3n = 81$
   giving $\qquad 3n = 70$
   70 is not a multiple of 3, so the solution is not an integer.
   Therefore, 81 is not in the sequence.

> Remember, n must be an integer.

Exam corner · Grade 5

1. The nth term of a sequence is $100 - 7n$

   a) Work out the 9th term of the sequence. **[I got __/1 mark]**

   b) Work out the first negative term of this sequence. **[__/2 marks]**

   c) Show that 50 is not a term of this sequence. **[__/2 marks]**

2. Part of a geometric sequence is given: 108, …, 12, 4, …
   Work out the 2nd and 5th terms. **[__/2 marks]** · Grade 6

> First find the value of n by solving the inequality $100 - 7n < 0$

Arithmetic sequences

You need to be able to find the rule for the nth term of an arithmetic sequence.

Key points

The nth term of an arithmetic sequence is a linear expression:

$$dn + c$$

where d and c are numbers that you have to work out.

To find the nth term:

> Work out the common difference between terms
>
> ↓
>
> Write out the multiples of the common difference
>
> ↓
>
> Work out what to add or subtract to get the original sequence, in this case 1, and write out the nth term rule
>
> ↓
>
> Check your answer by substituting in values of n

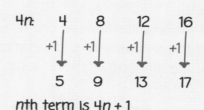

Common difference = 4

4n:

nth term is $4n + 1$

$n = 1$: $4 \times 1 + 1 = 5$ ✓

Worked example

Grade 4

Write an expression, in terms of n, for the nth term of the sequence.

5, 14, 23, 32, 41, … **[2 marks]**

Solution

Common difference = 9

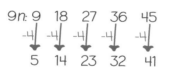

The nth term is $9n - 4$

Worked example

Grade 6

A teacher buys 60 pencils at the beginning of term. The number of pencils left at the end of each week forms an arithmetic sequence. After 3 weeks, he has 48 pencils remaining. Write an expression for the number of pencils after w weeks. **[2 marks]**

Solution

In 3 weeks, the number of pencils decreased by 12, so they are decreasing by 4 per week.
Number of pencils = $60 - 4w$

Exam corner

Grade 4

1. Write an expression, in terms of n, for the nth term of each of these sequences.

   a) 5, 3, 1, −1, −3, … **[I got __/2 marks]**

   b) $\frac{1}{2}$, 2, $3\frac{1}{2}$, 5, $6\frac{1}{2}$, … **[__/2 marks]**

2. Simon pays into a savings account each month. The amount he pays in each month forms an arithmetic sequence.

   In January he paid in £30 and in February he paid in £37

   a) Write an expression for the amount he paid into the account in the mth month of the year. **[__/2 marks]**

   Grade 6

   b) Work out the amount he paid into the account in December. **[__/2 marks]**

Examiner's tip!

Remember: always check your answer by substituting in $n = 1$

CLIMB TO 9 See pages 120–121 for more practice.

Quadratic sequences

The nth term of a quadratic sequence has an n^2 term.

Key points

In a quadratic sequence, the difference between the terms changes by the same amount each time.
To find the nth term:
STEP 1: Work out the second difference, and halve it.
STEP 2: Work out this number $\times n^2$ and subtract from each term.
STEP 3: Work out the nth term of the remaining linear sequence.
STEP 4: Put it all together.

To work out the second difference...

	3		5		10		18		29

1st differences: +2   +5   +8   +11

2nd differences: +3   +3   +3

Worked example

Grade 8

Part of a quadratic sequence is: 4, 5, 12, 25, …
Work out an expression for the nth term. **[3 marks]**

Solution

STEP 1: 4   5   12   25

+1   +7   +13

+6   +6

The second difference is 6. Halve this to give 3. The sequence involves $3n^2$.

STEP 2: Subtract $3n^2$ from each term of the original sequence:

	4	5	12	25
$-3n^2$:	3	12	27	48
	1	-7	-15	-23

STEP 3: Work out the nth term of the linear sequence:
1, -7, -15, -23, …
nth term is $-8n + 9$

STEP 4: Put it all together: nth term is $3n^2 - 8n + 9$

Check your final rule by substituting in a value for n.

Worked example

Grade 7

Write the nth term of each sequence.
a) 1, 4, 9, 16, 25, … **[1 mark]**
b) 2, 8, 18, 32, 50, … **[1 mark]**

Solution

a) These are the square numbers so the nth term is n^2.

b) The terms are double the square numbers, so the nth term is $2n^2$.

See page 49 for how to find the nth term of a linear sequence.

Exam corner

Grade 7

1. Here is a sequence of rectangles formed from squares.

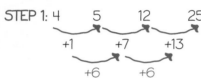

Pattern 1   Pattern 2   Pattern 3

If you're not confident with this topic, don't be distracted by the diagrams. Count the squares, list the terms numerically and follow Steps 1–4

Write an expression for the number of squares in the nth pattern. **[I got ___/2 marks]**

2. Work out the nth term of these quadratic sequences:

a) 1, 5, 11, 19, … **[___/3 marks]**   **b)** 1, 2, 7, 16, … **[___/3 marks]**

Grade 8

Iteration 1

Instead of using an algebraic method to solve an equation, sometimes you need to use a numerical method called **iteration**.

Key points

- If the value of a function changes from negative to positive (or vice versa), then there must be a root in that interval.
- Use an **iteration formula** to find an approximate solution to an equation. The formula gives x_{n+1} in terms of x_n. Each successive value is closer to the solution.
- x_0 is the starting value and will be given to you in the question.
- To use the iteration formula:

STEP 1: Substitute x_0 into the formula where it says x_n. This will give you x_1

STEP 2: Substitute x_1 in the same way to find x_2

STEP 3: Repeat until two consecutive answers are the same when rounded to the degree of accuracy given in the question.

> Remember this...
> Where there's a change of sign, there's a root...
>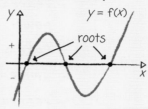

Calculator tip

You need to use your calculator efficiently for iteration questions. Start by typing in the value of x_0. In part **b** for example, start by pressing [2]. Then press [=]

Now enter the formula like this:

[2] [+] [1] [÷] [ANS] [x^2]

Then you can press [=] repeatedly to get $x_1, x_2, x_3, ...$

Worked example

a) Show that the equation $x^3 + x^2 - 3 = 0$ has a solution between $x = 1$ and $x = 2$ **[2 marks]**

b) Starting with $x_0 = 1$, use the iteration formula $x_{n+1} = \sqrt[3]{3 - (x_n)^2}$ to find an estimate, correct to 2 significant figures, for a solution of $x^3 + x^2 - 3 = 0$ **[3 marks]**

Solution

a) Substitute $x = 1$: $1^3 + 1^2 - 3 = -1$
Substitute $x = 2$: $2^3 + 2^2 - 3 = 9$
Since there's a change of sign, there must be a solution between $x = 1$ and $x = 2$

b) Use the iteration formula with $x_0 = 1$:
$x_1 = \sqrt[3]{3 - (1)^2} = 1.2599...$
$x_2 = \sqrt[3]{3 - (1.2599...)^2} = 1.1220...$
$x_3 = \sqrt[3]{3 - (1.1220...)^2} = 1.2030...$
$x_4 = \sqrt[3]{3 - (1.2030...)^2} = 1.1579...$

x_3 and x_4 are both 1.2 to 2 significant figures, so the estimate is $x \approx 1.2$

> First rearrange the equation so you have zero on one side.

Exam corner

1. a) Show that the equation $x^3 + x^2 = 5$ has a solution between $x = 1$ and $x = 2$
[I got ___ /2 marks]

b) Use the iteration formula $x_{n+1} = \sqrt{\dfrac{5}{x_n + 1}}$ with $x_0 = 1$ to find the values of x_1 and x_2 to 3 significant figures. **[___/2 marks]**

2. Use the iteration formula
$$x_{n+1} = 2 + \frac{1}{(x_n)^2}$$
with $x_0 = 2$ to find the solution to $x^3 - 2x^2 = 1$ correct to 3 significant figures. **[___/3 marks]**

Iteration 2

You can derive an iteration formula from the original equation.

Key points

An equation such as
$$x^3 - x^2 - 200 = 0$$
can be rearranged to give
$$x = \sqrt[3]{200 + x^2}$$
This gives the iteration formula
$$x_{n+1} = \sqrt[3]{200 + x_n^2}$$

To derive an iteration formula, look at what you're aiming for and try one or more of these strategies:

- rearrange to make the highest power of x the subject
- take a root
- divide by a power of x
- rearrange then factorise one side of the equation

Confidence bar

___

Sorted!

Had a look

Worked example

Grade 9

a) Show that the equation $x^3 + 7x - 1 = 0$ can be rearranged to give

$$x = \frac{1}{x^2 + 7}$$

[2 marks]

b) Starting with $x_0 = 1$, use the iteration formula

$$x_{n+1} = \frac{1}{(x_n)^2 + 7}$$

to find the value of x_3 to 3 significant figures. **[3 marks]**

The iteration formula given in part **b** involves $x^2 + 7$. Notice that the first two terms of the equation in part **a** will factorise to $x(x^2 + 7)$. This gives you a hint of how to rearrange the equation in part **a**.

Solution

a) Start with $x^3 + 7x - 1 = 0$

$$x^3 + 7x = 1$$
$$x(x^2 + 7) = 1$$
$$x = \frac{1}{x^2 + 7}$$

b) $x_0 = 1$

$$x_1 = \frac{1}{1^2 + 7} = \frac{1}{8}$$

$$x_2 = \frac{1}{\left(\frac{1}{8}\right)^2 + 7} = \frac{64}{449} = 0.1425\ldots$$

$$x_3 = \frac{1}{\left(\frac{64}{449}\right)^2 + 7} = 0.1424\ldots = 0.142 \text{ to 3 sf}$$

Exam corner

Grade 9

a) Show that the equation $2x^3 + x - 4 = 0$ has a solution between $x = 1$ and $x = 2$ **[I got ___/2 marks]**

b) Show that the equation $2x^3 + x - 4 = 0$ can be rearranged to give $x = \sqrt[3]{\frac{4-x}{2}}$ **[___/2 marks]**

c) Starting with $x_0 = 1$, use an iteration formula twice to find an estimate for a solution of $2x^3 + x - 4 = 0$ to an appropriate degree of accuracy. **[___/3 marks]**

Examiner's tip!

If you aren't able to derive a given iteration formula in the exam (part **b**), you should still try to use the formula you're given to find an approximate solution (part **c**).

To decide on the appropriate degree of accuracy, find the most accurate value that both x_1 and x_2 will round to.

Functions

A **function** is a relation between an input and an output.

Key points

- $f(x)$, $g(x)$, etc. are used to label functions, e.g. $f(x) = x^2$
- You can evaluate a function by substituting in a value of x, e.g. $f(3) = 3^2 = 9$
- Functions can be combined to form composite functions, e.g. $fg(x)$ or $f(g(x))$

Take care with the order of composite functions...

$fg(x)$ means function g <u>followed by</u> function f

If $f(x) = x^2$ and $g(x) = x + 2$

then $fg(x) = f(x + 2) = (x + 2)^2$ but $gf(x) = g(x^2) = x^2 + 2$

Confidence bar

Sorted!

☑
☑
☑

Had a look

Worked example

Grade 7

$f(x) = 4x^2 + 2x - 1$

a) Work out $f(-3)$ **[1 mark]**

b) Work out the values of x for which $f(x) = 1$ **[3 marks]**

Solution

a) $f(-3) = 4(-3)^2 + 2(-3) - 1$

$= 36 - 6 - 1 = 29$

b) $4x^2 + 2x - 1 = 1$

$4x^2 + 2x - 2 = 0$

$2x^2 + x - 1 = 0$

$(2x - 1)(x + 1) = 0$

$x = \frac{1}{2}$ or -1

> See page 26 for how to solve this quadratic equation.

Worked example

Grade 8

$f(x) = 2x + 1$, $g(x) = 5 - x^2$

a) Work out $gf(2)$ **[2 marks]**

b) Write a simplified expression for

i) $fg(x)$ **ii)** $ff(x)$ **[4 marks]**

c) Solve the equation $fg(x) = g(x)$

[2 marks]

Solution

a) Evaluate $f(2)$ first: $f(2) = 2(2) + 1 = 5$

Now, substitute into g:

$gf(2) = g(5) = 5 - 5^2 = -20$

b) **i)** $fg(x) = f(5 - x^2)$

$= 2(5 - x^2) + 1$

$= 11 - 2x^2$

ii) $ff(x) = f(2x + 1)$

$= 2(2x + 1) + 1$

$= 4x + 3$

c) $11 - 2x^2 = 5 - x^2$

$x^2 = 6$

$x = \sqrt{6}$ or $-\sqrt{6}$

Exam corner

Grade 6

1. The function f is such that $f(x) = \dfrac{x + 1}{4}$

a) Work out $f(7)$

[I got __ /1 mark]

b) Work out the value of x for which $f(x) = 5$

[__/2 marks]

Grade 8

2. $f(x) = x^2 - 2$, $g(x) = 2x + 1$

a) Work out $f(-5)$ **[__/1 mark]**

b) Show that $fg(x) = 4x^2 + 4x - 1$ **[__/2 marks]**

c) Solve the equation $gf(x) = fg(x)$ **[__/3 marks]**

Remember, in general,
$$fg(x) \neq gf(x)$$
In this question, you need to find the value of x for which they are equal.

Inverse functions

The **inverse** of a function reverses its effect; you can use algebra to find an inverse.

Key points

- The inverse of f(x) is written $f^{-1}(x)$.
- $ff^{-1}(x) = f^{-1}f(x) = x$
- Follow these steps to find the inverse of f(x):
  STEP 1: Write in the form $y = ...$
  STEP 2: Rearrange to make x the subject
  STEP 3: Replace every y with an x and write as $f^{-1}(x) = ...$

You can also use a function machine to find the inverse of simple functions...

e.g. if $f(x) = 3x - 7$

$$x \rightarrow \boxed{\times 3} \rightarrow \boxed{- 7} \rightarrow f(x)$$

$$f^{-1}(x) \leftarrow \boxed{\div 3} \leftarrow \boxed{+ 7} \leftarrow x$$

$$f^{-1}(x) = \frac{x + 7}{3}$$

Worked example

The function f is such that $f(x) = 9 - 5x$

a) Work out an expression for $f^{-1}(x)$ **[2 marks]**
b) Solve the equation $f(x) = f^{-1}(x)$ **[3 marks]**

Solution

a) STEP 1: Let $y = 9 - 5x$

STEP 2: $5x = 9 - y$

$$x = \frac{9 - y}{5}$$

STEP 3: $f^{-1}(x) = \dfrac{9 - x}{5}$

b) $9 - 5x = \dfrac{9 - x}{5}$

$45 - 25x = 9 - x$

$36 = 24x$

$x = \dfrac{36}{24} = 1.5$

Exam corner

1. Work out the inverse function in each case.

   a) $f(x) = 11 + 3x$ **[I got ___ /2 marks]**

   b) $g(x) = 11 - \dfrac{3}{x}$, for $x \neq 0$ **[___/2 marks]**

   c) $h(x) = \dfrac{11 - 3x}{x}$, for $x \neq 0$ **[___/3 marks]**

2. The function g is such that
   $g(x) = x^2 - kx$ for $x > 3$
   Given that $g(7) = 7$

   a) Work out the value of k **[___/2 marks]**

   b) Work out an expression for $g^{-1}(x)$ **[___/3 marks]**

Worked example

$f(x) = 5x - 2$, $g(x) = x^3 + 1$
The function h is such that $h(x) \equiv gf(x)$

a) Work out an expression for $h^{-1}(x)$ **[3 marks]**
b) Given that $h(a) = 9$, work out the value of a **[3 marks]**

Solution

a) First find h(x):
   $h(x) = g(5x - 2)$

   $= (5x - 2)^3 + 1$

   STEP 1: Let $y = (5x - 2)^3 + 1$

   STEP 2: $y - 1 = (5x - 2)^3$

   $\sqrt[3]{y - 1} = 5x - 2$

   $2 + \sqrt[3]{y - 1} = 5x$

   $x = \dfrac{1}{5}(2 + \sqrt[3]{y - 1})$

   STEP 3: $h^{-1}(x) = \dfrac{1}{5}(2 + \sqrt[3]{x - 1})$

b) $h(a) = 9$ implies that

   $a = h^{-1}(9)$

   $= \dfrac{1}{5}(2 + \sqrt[3]{9 - 1})$

   $= 0.8$

> Make sure your final answer is in terms of x.

> Try completing the square.
> See page 28

Algebraic proof

To disprove a statement, you just need to give a single example where it doesn't work. But to prove a statement, you need to use algebra.

Key points

- An **equation** is only true for certain values, e.g. $x + 5 = 8$ is only true for $x = 3$
- An **identity** is true for all values, e.g. $2x + 3x = 5x$, so you can write $2x + 3x \equiv 5x$
- To prove an identity, start with the expression on one side and use algebraic techniques such as expanding and simplifying until you reach the expression on the other side.

Remember this...

Equation	Identity
$=$	$\equiv$
equal for certain values	equal for all values

Worked example

Grade 6

a) Prove that $(a + b)^2 - (a - b)^2 \equiv 4ab$ **[3 marks]**

b) Anis claims that the difference between two square numbers is always even. Give a counter-example to disprove her claim. **[2 marks]**

Solution

a) Start with the left-hand side (LHS).

$$LHS \equiv (a + b)^2 - (a - b)^2$$
$$\equiv (a^2 + 2ab + b^2) - (a^2 - 2ab + b^2)$$
$$\equiv \cancel{a^2} + 2ab + \cancel{b^2} - \cancel{a^2} + 2ab - \cancel{b^2}$$
$$\equiv 4ab$$
$$\equiv RHS \quad \text{(right-hand side)}$$

b) Pick two square numbers such as 4 and 9 The difference between them is 5. This is odd, which disproves Anis's claim that the difference between two square numbers is always even.

Worked example

Grade 8

Prove that the difference between the squares of any two consecutive odd numbers is always a multiple of 8 **[4 marks]**

Solution

Let n be an integer.

Then $2n + 1$ and $2n + 3$ are consecutive odd numbers.

> If n is an integer, then you can use $2n$ to represent even numbers and $2n + 1$ to represent odd numbers.

Difference between the squares

$$= (2n + 3)^2 - (2n + 1)^2$$
$$\equiv (4n^2 + 12n + 9) - (4n^2 + 4n + 1)$$
$$\equiv 8n + 8$$
$$\equiv 8(n + 1)$$

> To show an expression is a multiple of a number you must write it with the number as a factor.

Exam corner

Grade 7

1. a) Give a counter-example to disprove the statement: 'If $a > b$, then $a^2 > b^2$' **[I got ___/2 marks]**

b) Prove that $(3n + 2)^2 - (3n + 1)^2$ is a multiple of 3 for all positive integer values of n **[___/3 marks]**

2. Prove algebraically that the product of any two odd numbers is odd. **[___/3 marks]**

Grade 8

Examiner's tip!

In a proof question do not use substitution to show the statement is true for specific values. You must use algebra to prove it is true for <u>all</u> values.

See pages 120–121 for more practice

Ratio

Ratio is a neat way of comparing two or more quantities. You can use a ratio to solve problems.

Key points

- A ratio can be simplified fully by dividing both sides by their highest common factor (HCF).
- Ratio problems can sometimes be solved by 'scaling up' a ratio. You do this by multiplying both sides by the same number
- A ratio can be expressed as a fraction, e.g. if the ratio of adults to children is 1:2 then $\frac{1}{3}$ of the total are adults and $\frac{2}{3}$ are children.
- Ratios can also have three or more parts, *for example a:b:c*

Using bar models to answer ratio problems

To share £90 in the ratio 1:5:3, draw a bar model split in the ratio 1:5:3

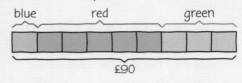

There are 9 boxes, so each will be worth £10 to make a total of £90. Now you can see by counting squares that the amounts of each share are £10, £50 and £30

Worked example

Grade 4

A shade of purple paint is made by mixing blue, red and white paint in the ratio 5:3:1

How much red and white paint would you need to add to 120 ml of blue paint to make this shade of purple paint? **[3 marks]**

Solution

Ratio blue:red:white = 5:3:1

You need to scale up the ratio by multiplying each part by 24 (since 120 ÷ 5 = 24).

Then blue:red:white = 120:72:24

You need 72 ml of red paint and 24 ml of white paint.

Worked example

Grade 5

The ratio of pigs to chickens on a farm is 2:5 There are 24 more chickens than pigs. Work out the total number of each animal. **[3 marks]**

Solution

There are 24 more chickens than pigs so these three blocks must add up to 24. Each block is worth 8

There are 2 × 8 = 16 pigs and 5 × 8 = 40 chickens.

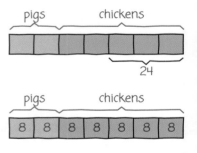

Exam corner

1. Mortar can be made by mixing water, cement and sand in the ratio 1:2:3

   How much water, cement and sand will be needed to make 27 kg of mortar? **[I got ___/3 marks]**

   Grade 4

2. A recipe for shortbread biscuits needs sugar, flour and butter. The ratio of sugar to butter is 2:5 and you need three times as much flour as sugar. A single shortbread biscuit weighs 26 g. Work out how much butter is needed to make 12 biscuits. **[___/4 marks]**

   Grade 5

Examiner's tip!

Check that the total of the three quantities is correct. Here the three amounts must add up to 27

CLIMB TO 9   See pages 122-123 for more practice

Harder ratio problems

Grade
6–8

Harder ratio problems may involve fractions and percentages.

Key points

Using fractions and percentages with ratio:

- If $a:b = 3:5$, then $\dfrac{a}{b} = \dfrac{3}{5}$
- If b is 20% less than a, then $a:b = 100:80$ which is $5:4$
- If $2a = 3b$, then $a:b = \dfrac{3}{2}:1$ which is $3:2$ (be careful here: a is greater than b).

In some problems you may need to form a linear equation and solve it.

Confidence bar

Sorted!

☑

☑

☑

Had a look

Worked example

Grade
6

Harry and Laura share £84. Laura receives 10% more than Harry. How much did Harry receive? **[3 marks]**

Solution

Write the ratio of the amounts they received.

Harry:Laura = 100:110 = 10:11

One part = 84 ÷ (10 + 11) = £4

Amount Harry received = 10 × 4 = £40

Worked example

The ratio of blue to red counters in a box is $3:1$.

Two counters are removed from the box. The probability of removing two red counters is $\dfrac{1}{17}$

Work out the number of red counters that were in the box initially. **[5 marks]**

Grade
8

Solution

Let x be the number of red counters initially.

Total number of counters initially = $4x$

Initially, P(red) = $\dfrac{1}{4}$

Then, if a red counter is removed, number of red counters = $x - 1$ and total number of counters = $4x - 1$

P(two reds) = $\dfrac{1}{4} \times \dfrac{x-1}{4x-1}$

$\dfrac{1}{4} \times \dfrac{x-1}{4x-1} = \dfrac{1}{17}$ as given

$17(x - 1) = 4(4x - 1)$

$17x - 17 = 16x - 4$

$x = 13$

Number of red counters initially = 13

See pages 109 and 110 for more on probability with two events.

In questions where the ratio changes:

> Write both situations as equations with fractions.

⬇

> Form linear equations.

⬇

> Solve the equations simultaneously (see page 22).

Examiner's tip!

CLIMB TO 9

Before you finish: Check the values you have found work with the ratios given in the question.

Exam corner

Grade
7

1. x is three-quarters of y, and $3y = 2z$. Write the ratio $x:y:z$ in its simplest form, where x, y and z are integers. **[I got ___/3 marks]**

2. The ratio of milk to cream in a chocolate mousse recipe is $2:1$. Jacob decides to replace 50 ml of the milk with cream so the ratio becomes $3:2$. What were the quantities of milk and cream in the original recipe? **[___/5 marks]**

Grade
8

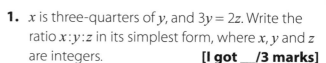

CLIMB TO 9
See pages 122–123 for more practice

Percentage change

Without using a calculator, you need to be able to find the new value after a percentage change. You also need to be able to work out the percentage change that has taken place based on the before and after values.

Key points

There are three kinds of calculation with percentage change:

1) To find the value after a percentage increase, work out the increase then add it onto the original amount.

2) To find the value after a percentage decrease, work out the decrease then subtract it from the original amount.

3) To work out the percentage change that has taken place, divide the change in the amount by the **original amount**.

To find the **percentage increase**: $\dfrac{\text{actual increase}}{\text{original amount}}$

To find the **percentage decrease**: $\dfrac{\text{actual decrease}}{\text{original amount}}$ $\Big\} \rightarrow \times 100\%$

Worked example

Grade 3

Work out the total of this restaurant bill, including the service charge of 12%.

[2 marks]

Food + drinks £70.
Plus service charge of 12%

Solution

10% of £70 is £7

1% of £70 is £0.70, so 2% is £1.40

Then 12% of £70 is £7 + £1.40 = £8.40

The bill will increase by 12% so add this amount:

Total = £70 + £8.40 = £78.40

Worked example

Grade 4

A car's value decreases from £12 000 to £9000 over the first year after it is produced.
Work out the percentage decrease. **[2 marks]**

Solution

The actual decrease in value is

£12 000 − £9000 = £3000

The percentage decrease is

$$\frac{3\cancel{000}}{12\cancel{000}} \times 100\% = 25\%$$

Exam corner

Grade 3

1. The cost for a child to use a climbing wall is 40% less than the cost for an adult. The cost for an adult is £25. Work out the cost for a child. **[I got __/2 marks]**

Grade 4

2. The cost of school dinner increased over the summer holiday from £2.20 to £2.53
Work out the percentage increase in cost.
Circle the correct answer.

   1.2%   13%   14%   15%   **[__/1 mark]**

Examiner's tip!

You can check by increasing £2.20 by your answer. If you get £2.53, you found the right percentage increase.

Using multipliers

You can use a **multiplier** to solve problems involving percentage increase and decrease.

Key points

- To find the **multiplier** for a problem, write the percentage as a decimal.
- You can then **multiply** by the multiplier to find the value **after** a percentage change.
- Or **divide** by the multiplier to find the value **before** a percentage change.

To **increase** by a percentage (e.g. 8%), **add** the percentage to 100 (e.g. 108)

To **decrease** by a percentage, (e.g. 8%) **subtract** the percentage from 100, e.g. 92

Calculating a percentage change to an amount, e.g. 75

Divide this number by 100 to work out the **multiplier**. E.g. 1.08 or 0.92

Multiply this number by the original amount. E.g. 8% increase on 75 = 75 × 1.08 = 81

Confidence bar

Sorted!

☑
☑
☑

Had a look

Worked example $\quad$ Grade 4

Samuel takes 8% longer to run a race than Omar. Samuel completes the race in 48.6 seconds. Work out Omar's time. **[2 marks]**

Solution

The question is about percentage increase:
100% + 8% = 108% = 1.08
You need the value <u>before</u> the increase, so divide by the multiplier:
48.6 ÷ 1.08 = 45
Omar's time is 45 seconds.

Worked example $\quad$ Grade 6

The price of a TV, £450, is reduced by 12% in a sale. Greg also has a staff discount of 25% off all sale prices. How much does Greg pay for the TV?
[3 marks]

Solution

The question is about percentage decrease:
100% − 12% = 88% so the first multiplier is 0.88
100% − 25% = 75% so the next multiplier is 0.75
You need the value <u>after</u> the decrease, so multiply:
450 × 0.88 × 0.75 = 297
Greg pays £297 for the TV.

Exam corner $\quad$ Grade 4

1. Tanya completed a logic puzzle in 196 seconds. This was a 30% improvement on her previous attempt. Work out her time on her previous attempt. **[I got __/2 marks]**

2. The cost of a season ticket for a football club increased by 5% two years ago, then increased by 8% last year. This year it costs £670. Work out the cost of a season ticket two years ago, to the nearest £. **[__/3 marks]** $\quad$ Grade 6

Watch out for this type of question – you can't just add up the two discounts to get 37% because the second discount is applied to the sale price.

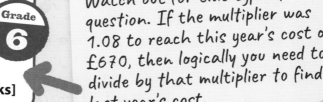

Watch out for this type of question. If the multiplier was 1.08 to reach this year's cost of £670, then logically you need to divide by that multiplier to find last year's cost.

Growth and depreciation

There is a formula you can use when percentage increases and decreases are repeated.

Key points

- **Simple interest** is where you only earn interest on the initial investment.
- **Compound interest** is where the interest is left in the account and earns interest itself.

Formula box

To increase/decrease an amount, A, by the same percentage n times, use

$$A \times (\text{multiplier})^n$$

 See page 59 for how to work out the multiplier.

Worked example

Grade 6

Natalie keeps £3500 in a savings account for 5 years, at an interest rate of 4% per year. She needs to decide whether to take the interest out of the account each year or leave it in. Work out how much extra interest she will earn if she leaves it in. **[5 marks]**

Solution

If she takes it out, it is **simple interest**:
4% of £3500 = 0.04 × 3500 = £140
Total interest for 5 years = £140 × 5 = £700
If she leaves it in, it is **compound interest**:
100% + 4% = 104% ⟹ 1.04 is the multiplier.
Total in account after 5 years = 3500 × 1.04^5
= £4258.29
Total interest for 5 years = 4258.29 – 3500
= £758.29
Difference = £758.29 – £700 = £58.29

Worked example

Grade 7

The population of a type of fish in a lake is decreasing by x% each year. The population is initially 700. After three years the population is 525. Work out the value of x to 1 decimal place.
[3 marks]

Solution

Using the formula, you know that
700 × $(\text{multiplier})^3$ = 525
$(\text{multiplier})^3$ = 0.75
multiplier = $\sqrt[3]{0.75}$ = 0.9085...
So, (100 – x)% = 90.85...%
x = 9.1 to 1 decimal place

Check your answer by reducing 700 by 9.1% three times. Your answer should be close to 525 (not exactly 525, because of rounding).

Exam corner

Grade 6

1. The population of a town is estimated to be increasing by 3% each year.

At the beginning of 2020, the population of the town is 32 000. Estimate the population to the nearest 1000 at the beginning of 2030
[I got __/3 marks]

Grade 7

2. The value of a bike depreciates by 30% in the first year, then by x% each following year.

The bike was originally bought for £400. After three years the value of the bike is £200. Work out the value of x to 1 decimal place. **[__/4 marks]**

Compound measures

A compound measure links two measurements. For example, a rate of pay could be £11 per hour and a rate of flow of water could be 3 litres per minute.

Formula box

Speed, **density** and **pressure** are three compound measures you need to be familiar with.

You can use the triangles here to remember how to work these out.

Cover up the measurement you want to work out and then either multiply or divide.

$$Speed = \frac{Distance}{Time}$$

$$Density = \frac{Mass}{Volume}$$

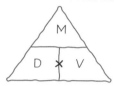

$$Pressure = \frac{Force}{Area}$$

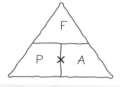

Remember these...

Speed is in **miles** (distance) **per hour** (time).
Per means divide, so speed = distance ÷ time.

I ♥ Density!
$$D = \frac{♥}{♥}$$

Fly
Pilots → Aeroplanes

Worked example

Grade 5

What is the size of force required to exert a pressure of 7 N/cm² on an area of 54 cm²?

[2 marks]

Solution

Draw the triangle and cover up F
Force = **Pressure** × **Area**
= 7 × 54
= 378 N

Worked example

Grade 5

The density of a piece of wood is 2.4 g/cm³ and its mass is 1.8 kg.
Work out the volume of the wood. **[3 marks]**

Solution

1.8 kg = 1800 g

Draw the triangle and cover up V
$$Volume = \frac{Mass}{Density} = \frac{1800}{2.4}$$
$$= 750 \, cm^3$$

Exam corner

Grade 4

1. **a)** Work out the time taken to travel 9 m at a speed of 0.3 m/s. **[I got __/2 marks]**

   b) A car is driving at 54 km/h. Work out the distance in metres covered by the car in 10 s. **[__/3 marks]**

2. A force of 24 N is applied to an area of 400 000 cm². Work out the pressure.
   Circle the correct answer.
   0.6 N/m²   1.7 N/m²   0.006 N/m²   167 N/m²   **[__/1 mark]**

Grade 5

Examiner's tip! **CLIMB TO 9**

Always check the units. You may need to convert one of the measures before you can complete the calculation.

CLIMB TO 9 See pages 116–117 for more practice.

Direct & inverse proportion 1

Two values in **direct proportion** will increase and decrease at the same rate. If two values are **in inverse proportion**, one will increase at the same rate that the other decreases.

Key points

- To solve a **direct proportion problem**, you can use the unitary method:
  STEP 1: Divide to work out the value of 1 unit.
  STEP 2: Multiply to find the value required.

  Alternatively, you can use ratios to solve the problem.
- To solve an **inverse proportion problem**, you often need to work out the number of 'man-hours' to complete the task.

Worked example

 Grade 4

It takes eight cleaners 3 hours to clean a block of offices.

a) How long does it take six cleaners to clean the offices? **[2 marks]**

b) How many cleaners are needed to clean the offices in 1.5 hours? **[2 marks]**

Solution

a) Total 'worker-hours' = 8 × 3 = 24

It will take 6 cleaners 24 ÷ 6 = 4 hours.

b) To clean the offices in 1.5 hours,

24 ÷ 1.5 = 16 cleaners are needed.

A graph showing **direct proportion** is a straight line through the origin.

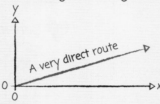

The equation is $y = kx$, where k is any number.

A graph showing **inverse proportion** will curve in near the origin.

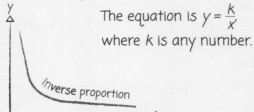

The equation is $y = \dfrac{k}{x}$, where k is any number.

Exam corner

 Grade 4

Grade 5

1. On a particular day, 100 Indian rupees was worth 150 Japanese yen.

   a) Draw an exchange rate graph, with values of rupees from 0 to 200 **[I got ___/3 marks]**

   b) Work out the value of 120 yen in rupees. **[___/2 marks]**

2. It takes 12 gardeners 5 hours to plant some trees alongside a new stretch of motorway.

   a) How long would it take 15 gardeners to plant the trees? **[___/2 marks]**

   b) How many gardeners would be needed to plant the trees in 2 hours? **[___/2 marks]**

   c) Draw a graph to show the relationship between the number of gardeners, g, and the time taken to plant the trees, t **[___/2 marks]**

Direct & inverse proportion 2

You can form equations to link variables that are in direct or inverse proportion.

Key points

- If x is directly proportional to y, then $y = kx$
- If x is inversely proportional to y, then $y = \dfrac{k}{x}$
- k is called the **constant of proportionality**.
- It is also possible for y to be directly or inversely proportional to a function of x, for example, $y = kx^3$ or $y = \dfrac{k}{\sqrt{x}}$

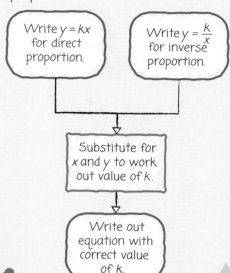

To form equations that describe proportion:

Write $y = kx$ for direct proportion.

Write $y = \dfrac{k}{x}$ for inverse proportion.

Substitute for x and y to work out value of k.

Write out equation with correct value of k.

Worked example

Grade 7

y is inversely proportional to x^2

$y = 2$ when $x = 3$

Work out the value of y when $x = 4$ **[3 marks]**

Solution

Write correct equation: $y = \dfrac{k}{x^2}$

Substitute x and y: $2 = \dfrac{k}{9}$

Work out value of k: $k = 18$

Write out equation: $y = \dfrac{18}{x^2}$

When $x = 4$, $y = \dfrac{18}{4^2}$

$= \dfrac{9}{8}$

Worked example

Grade 8

The length of a pendulum, L, is directly proportional to the square root of T, the time for one swing. Work out how a decrease of 10% in the length will affect the time for one swing.   **[3 marks]**

Solution

Write correct equation: $L = k\sqrt{T}$

You can't find the value of k here.

L is decreased by 10%, so multiply both sides by 0.9:

$$0.9L = 0.9k\sqrt{T}$$

To get this into the correct form, 0.9 needs to be inside the square root:

$$0.9L = k\sqrt{0.81T}$$

So, you can see that T becomes $0.81T$.

The time for one swing will decrease by 19%.

 See page 59 for more on multipliers and page 9 for more on surds.

Exam corner

1. V is inversely proportional to P

    $V = 6$ when $P = 18$

    Work out the value of P when $V = 4$

    [I got ___/3 marks]

    Grade 7

2. p is inversely proportional to r

    r is proportional to the square root of s

    $p = 1$ and $s = 36$ when $r = 3$

    Work out a formula for p in terms of s

    [___/4 marks]

    Grade 8

Form two equations and use the values given for p, s and r to find the constant of proportionality in each.

Measures

You need to be able to convert between different units, including those for area and volume.

Key points

Learn how to convert between these common **metric units**:

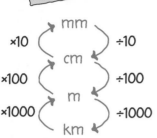
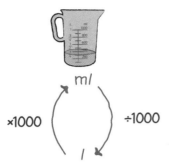

You might also need to convert between metric and **imperial units** (such as inches, miles, ounces, stones and pints), but you don't need to memorise those conversions.

Worked example

Grade 5

A sphere has a volume of 20 cm³ and a surface area of 36 cm².

a) Write the surface area in mm². **[2 marks]**

b) Write the volume in mm³. **[2 marks]**

Solution

To convert from cm to mm, you multiply by 10. So,

a) to convert from cm² to mm², multiply by 10^2:

surface area = $36 \times 10^2 = 3600 \text{ mm}^2$

b) to convert from cm³ to mm³, multiply by 10^3:

volume = $20 \times 10^3 = 20\,000 \text{ mm}^3$

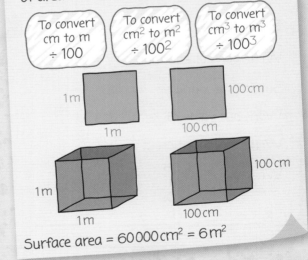

You need to be careful converting units of area and volume. For example:

To convert cm to m ÷ 100

To convert cm² to m² ÷ 100^2

To convert cm³ to m³ ÷ 100^3

Surface area = $60\,000 \text{ cm}^2 = 6 \text{ m}^2$

See page 61 for more on speed, distance and time.

Exam corner

Grade 5

1. Isaac is driving at a constant speed of 39 km/h.

a) Convert the speed to m/s. Give your answer to 1 decimal place. **[I got ___/2 marks]**

Isaac has 25 minutes to get to a meeting which is 11 miles away.

b) Use the conversion 1 mile ≈ 1.6 km to show that he will be late for the meeting if he continues at his constant speed. **[___/3 marks]**

Grade 6

2. A cylindrical flask has an internal surface area of 93 000 mm² and a capacity of 2.2 litres.

a) Work out the volume of the flask in mm³. **[___/2 marks]**

The inside of the flask is to be covered in a special coating which costs 0.3 p/cm².

b) Work out the cost of the coating. **[___/2 marks]**

See pages 124–125 for more practice

CLIMB TO 9

Angle rules

There are rules you can use to work out the size of unknown angles in different situations.

Key points

- Angles on a straight line add up to 180°.

- Angles around a point add up to 360°.

- **Vertically opposite** angles are equal.

- **Corresponding** angles are equal.

- **Alternate** angles are equal.

Remember these...

Corresponding angles are the same (corresponding) side of the transversal line (the line that cuts through the parallel line).

Alternate angles are alternate sides of the transversal line.

Worked example

Grade 5

Work out the value of x, giving geometrical reasons. **[3 marks]**

Solution

$\angle AGH = 180 - (x + 20)$ Angles on a line add up to 180°.

$= 160 - x$

$(x - 10) + 90 = 160 - x$ Corresponding angles are equal.

$x + 80 = 160 - x$

$2x = 80$

$x = 40°$

Exam corner

Grade 5

Work out the values of x and y, giving geometrical reasons.

[I got __/4 marks]

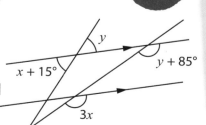

You will need to form and solve simultaneous equations here – see page 22

Examiner's tip!

If you're asked to give reasons, make sure you do so. And always use the proper names of angles.

Triangles & quadrilaterals

You need to know some properties of different triangles and quadrilaterals and use them to solve problems.

Grade 3-6

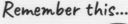

Remember this...
three sides the same **E**quilateral
two sides the same **I**sosceles

Key points

- Angles in a **triangle** add up to 180°.

Equilateral	Isosceles	Scalene	Right-angled
all sides equal all angles equal	two sides equal two angles equal	no sides equal no angles equal	has a 90° angle

- Angles in a **quadrilateral** add up to 360°.

Square Rectangle Kite Rhombus Parallelogram Trapezium

Confidence bar

Sorted!
☑
☑
☑

Had a look

Worked example

Grade 6

Shape **ABCD** is a parallelogram.
Work out the values of x and y **[4 marks]**

Solution

$\angle DAB = \angle BCD$ and $\angle CDA + \angle DAB = 180°$
since opposite angles of parallelograms are equal
and the sum of all angles is 360°.
$4x + 15 = 3x + 4y \Rightarrow x - 4y = -15$ (1)
$2y + 4x + 15 = 180 \Rightarrow 4x + 2y = 165$ (2)

Solve these equations simultaneously:
(1) × 4: $4x - 16y = -60$ (3)
(2) - (3): $4x + 2y = 165$
$\qquad 4x - 16y = -60 \Rightarrow 18y = 225$
$\qquad\qquad y = 12.5°$

Substitute into (1): $x - 4(12.5) = -15 \Rightarrow x = 35°$

 See page 22 for simultaneous equations.

Exam corner

Grade 5

1. The diagram shows a kite.
   Work out the value of x
   Circle the correct answer.
   30°   18°   24°   22.5°

   [I got __/1 mark]

2. Work out the size of the angle marked y in this diagram.
   Give a reason for each step in your working. **[__/4 marks]**

   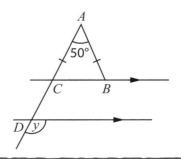

   Grade 6

66

Polygons

Polygons are 2D shapes with straight edges only. In addition to triangles and quadrilaterals, you need to know about some other common polygons.

Remember these...

A **pentagon** has 5 sides – you hold a pen in your 5-fingered hand.

A **hexagon** has 6 sides – think of the x: hex ⇒ six.

A **heptagon** has 7 sides – a heptathlon has 7 events.

An **octagon** has 8 sides – think of an octopus with 8 legs.

A **decagon** has 10 sides – think of a decade (10 years).

Key points

- A polygon can be **regular** or **irregular**.
- A **regular polygon** has all sides equal and all angles equal.
- The exterior angles of any polygon add up to 360°.

- To work out what the **interior angles** of any polygon add up to, use the rule:

  sum of interior angles = $(n - 2) \times 180$

  where n is the number of sides on the polygon.
- For any polygon, interior angle + exterior angle = 180°.
- A regular polygon with n sides will have n **lines of symmetry** and **order of rotational symmetry** n

E.g. for a hexagon:
sum of interior angles
= $(6 - 2) \times 180$
= 720°

The order of rotational symmetry is how many times an object fits perfectly into itself when going through a full rotation.

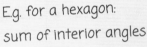

Worked example

The diagram shows a regular octagon.

Work out the value of x

[3 marks]

Solution

Sum of interior angles of octagon = $(8 - 2) \times 180$
  = 1080°

Interior angle of octagon = $1080 \div 8 = 135°$

$180 - 135 = 45°$

$x = 45 \div 2$ since triangle is isosceles
  = 22.5°

Exam corner

1. The size of each interior angle of a regular polygon is 156°. Work out how many sides the polygon has. Circle the correct answer.

   14   15   16   17   **[I got __/1 mark]**

2. The diagram shows a regular pentagon and a regular hexagon that meet along one edge. Work out the size of angle x **[__/3 marks]**

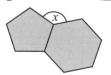

Circle theorems 1

Circle theorems enable you to solve problems involving angles in circles.

Key points

Angles in the same segment are equal.

Angle in a semicircle is a right angle.

Angle at centre is twice angle at circumference.

Opposite angles in a **cyclic quadrilateral** add up to 180°.

All the vertices of a **cyclic quadrilateral** lie on the circumference of a circle.

See page 74 for the definitions of the parts of a circle.

Worked example

Grade 8

A, B and C are points on the circumference of a circle. The centre of the circle is O

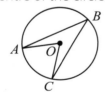

a) Prove that ∠AOC = 2 × ∠ABC
   [4 marks]

b) Given that ∠ABC = 35°, work out the size of ∠CAO
   [2 marks]

Solution

a) Split the quadrilateral into two triangles and label angles:

In △ABO, AO = OB, so △ is isosceles.
Let ∠OBA = x
∠AOB = 180 − 2x (∠s in isosceles △)
So, ∠DOA = 180 − (180 − 2x) = 2x

Similarly, use △BCO to show that ∠DOC = 2y

Then, ∠ABC = x + y and
∠AOC = 2x + 2y = 2∠ABC as required.

b) ∠AOC = 2 × ∠ABC = 2 × 35 = 70°
△CAO is isosceles since AO = OC
∠CAO = (180 − 70) ÷ 2 = 55°

Exam corner

Grade 7

1. Work out the size of angle y
   Give a reason for your answer.
   [I got ___/2 marks]

2. Prove that opposite angles of a cyclic quadrilateral add up to 180°. You can use the fact that angles in the same segment of a circle are equal.
   [___/3 marks]

Grade 8

Examiner's tip!

Make sure you explain your working clearly and state any circle theorems used.

For Question 2, start by drawing a cyclic quadrilateral and add in the diagonals.

Circle theorems 2

There are some circle theorems related to tangents to circles that you need to know and use.

Key points

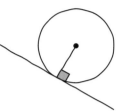

Angle between tangent and radius is 90°.

Two tangents from same point are equal in length.

Alternate segment theorem:

The angle between a tangent and a chord is equal to the angle from the chord in the alternate segment of the circle.

Worked example

Work out the size of angles x and y
State any circle theorems that you use. **[4 marks]**

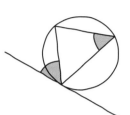

Solution

Obtuse $\angle BOD = 360 - 206 = 154°$

So, $x = 154 \div 2 = 77°$ Angle at centre is 2 × angle at circumference.

$\angle ABO = \angle ADO = 90°$ Angle between tangent and radius is 90°.

So, $y = 360 - 90 - 90 - 154$
    $= 26°$ Angles in quadrilateral add up to 360°.

Grade
8

To prove the alternate segment theorem, you will need to use these other theorems:

- angle at centre is 2 × angle at circumference
- angle between tangent and radius is 90°.

Exam corner

Grade
8

1. The line segment **DE** is a tangent to the circle at the point **C**. Given that $y = 38°$, work out the size of angle x

   Give reasons for your answer.
   [I got ___/3 marks]

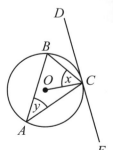

2. Using the diagram in Question 1, prove the alternate segment theorem. **[___/4 marks]**

Grade
9

Transformations

There are four transformations you need to know about. The first three are **rotation**, **reflection** and **translation**.

Key points

A **rotation** is described by giving:
- the angle (e.g. 90°)
- the direction (e.g. clockwise)
- the centre of rotation (e.g. the origin or another point).

A **reflection** is described by giving the equation of the mirror line.
A **translation** can be described using a **column vector**:

$\binom{2}{3}$ tells you to move 2 right and 3 up.

$\binom{-2}{-3}$ tells you to move 2 left and 3 down.

When you rotate, reflect or translate a shape, the object and its image are **congruent** (exactly the same shape and size).

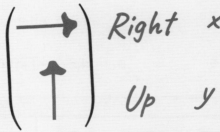

Right   x

Up   y

Negative values tell you to move left or down.

Worked example

Grade 4

Describe the transformations fully.

a) A to B **[3 marks]** **b)** A to C **[2 marks]**
c) A to D **[2 marks]**

Solution

a) Shape A has been moved right 2 and down 5, so this is:
a translation by the vector $\binom{2}{-5}$.

b) Shape A has been rotated 90°. You can use tracing paper to see that the centre of rotation is (1, 1). This is:
a rotation of 90° clockwise about (1, 1).

c) Shape A has been reflected. Draw on the mirror line and work out its equation ($y = -x$). This is:
a reflection in the line $y = -x$

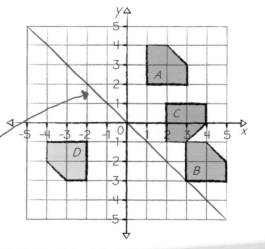

Exam corner

Grade 4

Using shape A in the Worked example:

a) rotate it 180° about the origin and label it E **[I got __/2 marks]**

b) reflect it in the line $x = 0$ and label it F **[__/2 marks]**

c) translate it by the vector $\binom{2}{0}$ and label it G **[__/1 mark]**

To reflect a shape, carefully reflect all the vertices separately, then join them up.

To translate a shape, you can just work out where one vertex will move to, then copy the rest of the shape in the same orientation.

Enlargement

Unlike the other transformations, the enlarged image of a shape is **similar** to but not always **congruent** to the object.

Key points

- To enlarge a shape by a positive **scale factor**, multiply the distance of each vertex from the **centre of enlargement** by the scale factor.
- Draw dotted lines from the centre of enlargement through the corresponding vertices of the object and the image.
- If the scale factor is a fraction between 0 and 1, the 'enlarged' shape will be smaller than the original.
- If the scale factor is negative, the image will be on the other side of the centre of enlargement and its orientation will change.

Worked example

Enlarge triangle T below by scale factor $\frac{1}{2}$ from centre of enlargement (1, 1).

[3 marks]

Solution

The distance from (1, 1) to each of the vertices of the image will be $\frac{1}{2}$ the distance to the original.

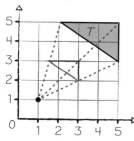

Confidence bar

Sorted!

☑

☑

☑

Had a look

If shapes are similar, they are in proportion to each other.

Worked example

Enlarge triangle A by scale factor −2, centre (0, 0).

[3 marks]

Solution

Draw dotted lines from each of the vertices of the triangle through the centre of enlargement.

The distance from the centre of enlargement to each of the vertices is multiplied by 2, but in the opposite direction from the centre.

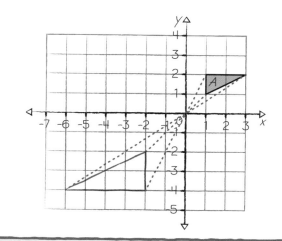

Exam corner

Grade 6

Grade 7

1. **a)** Enlarge shape A in the Worked example by scale factor −1, centre (−1, 2), and label the image B **[I got ___ /3 marks]**

   b) Fully describe another transformation that maps A to B **[___ /2 marks]**

2. On a coordinate grid, draw a rectangle C with vertices at (2, 1), (5, 1), (5, 7) and (2, 7). Enlarge C by scale factor $\frac{1}{3}$, centre (−1, 1), then reflect in the line $y = x$. Label the final image D **[___ /3 marks]**

Congruent shapes

Congruent shapes are exactly the same shape and size.

Key points

Congruent shapes have all corresponding sides equal and all angles equal.

Triangles are congruent if they meet one of these conditions:

SSS: All three sides match.

SAS: Two sides and the angle between them match.

ASA: Two angles and any side match.

RHS: Both are right-angled triangles, hypotenuse and one other side match.

Remember this...
Congruent triangles must meet one of these conditions:
SSS, SAS, ASA, RHS.

Not an ASS!

Nor AAA!

Confidence bar

Sorted!

Had a look

Worked example

ABCD is a parallelogram. The diagonals of *ABCD* meet at *E*

Prove that triangle *ABE* is congruent to triangle *CDE* **[3 marks]**

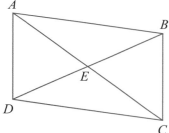

Solution

AB = DC since *ABCD* is a parallelogram.

$\angle EAB = \angle ECD$ since alternate angles are equal (*AB* and *DC* are parallel).

Similarly, $\angle ABE = \angle CDE$

Therefore, *ABE* and *CDE* have angle-side-angle (ASA) corresponding, so are congruent.

Examiner's tip!

Make sure you know all the angle rules on pages 65–67. In a proof always write any rules that you use.

Worked example

Given that the triangles are congruent,
a) state the length of *DE* **[1 mark]**
b) state the size of $\angle DEF$ **[1 mark]**

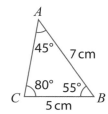

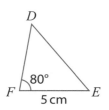

Solution

a) *DE* corresponds to *AB* since it is opposite the 80° angle.

DE = 7 cm

b) $\angle DEF = \angle ABC = 55°$

Exam corner

Triangle *ABC* is isosceles. *AD* is perpendicular to *CB*. Prove that triangles *ABD* and *ACD* are congruent.

[I got __/3 marks]

Look for an edge or an angle that is common to both.

Similar shapes

In maths, if we say shapes are **similar**, we mean they are in proportion to each other.

Grade
5–7

Key points

- **Similar** shapes have corresponding angles the same.
- They have corresponding side lengths in proportion, i.e. in the same ratio. The ratio is called the **scale factor**.

    $$\text{Scale factor (SF)} = \frac{\text{new length}}{\text{original length}}$$

- To find the area or volume of similar shapes, remember that every dimension will be multiplied by the scale factor, so:

    Multiply area by $(SF)^2$
    Multiply volume by $(SF)^3$

See page 64 for converting units of area and volume.

The two cubes are similar and the scale factor is 3

lengths ×3
areas ×9 (3^2)
volumes ×27 (3^3)

Confidence bar

Sorted!

☑
☑
☑

Had a look

Worked example

Grade 5

Triangles *ABC* and *ADE* are similar.

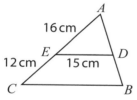

16 cm
12 cm   15 cm

Two shapes are similar if all their angles are the same.

Work out the length *CB* **[3 marks]**

Solution

First find the scale factor: $SF = \dfrac{AC}{AE} = \dfrac{28}{16} = 1.75$

$CB = 15 \times 1.75 = 26.25 \,\text{cm}$

Examiner's tip!

CLIMB TO 9

In questions like these it can help to draw the triangles out separately.

Worked example

Grade 7

A solid *A* is similar to a solid *B*. The surface area of *A* is 160 cm^2 and the surface area of *B* is 10 cm^2. The volume of *A* is 80 cm^3. Work out the volume of *B* **[3 marks]**

Solution

First work out what the surface area of *A* has been multiplied by. This will be the square of the scale factor:

$$(SF)^2 = \frac{10}{160} = \frac{1}{16}$$

Now find the scale factor:

$$SF = \sqrt{\frac{1}{16}} = \frac{1}{4}$$

Volume of *B* = $80 \times \left(\dfrac{1}{4}\right)^3 = 1.25 \,\text{cm}^3$

Exam corner

Grade 5

1. Triangles *VWX* and *VYZ* are similar. Work out the length *WY*
   [I got ___/3 marks]

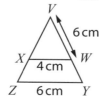

V
6 cm
X   W
4 cm
Z   6 cm   Y

Grade 7

2. Two similar shaped pieces of the same wood have mass 20 kg and 2.5 kg. The length of the longer piece is 60 cm. Work out the length of the shorter piece. **[___/3 marks]**

Mass is proportional to volume, so use $(SF)^3$

CLIMB TO 9 See pages 124-125 for more practice

Area and perimeter

Perimeter is calculated by adding all the lengths around the outside of a shape. **Area** is found by multiplying lengths together using a formula.

Formula box

Area of rectangle = base × height

= bh

Area of triangle = (base × height) ÷ 2

= $\frac{1}{2}bh$

Area of parallelogram = base × height

= bh

Area of trapezium = $\frac{1}{2}(a + b)h$

For a circle radius r (diameter d):

Circumference = $2\pi r$ (or πd)

Area = πr^2

Circumference

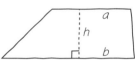

Remember this...

The formulae for circumference and area of a circle:

$C = \pi d$

<u>C</u>herry <u>p</u>ie is <u>d</u>elicious

$A = \pi r^2$

<u>A</u>pple <u>p</u>ies <u>a</u>re <u>2</u>

Worked example

Grade
4

The area of the trapezium is 42 cm². Work out the perimeter. **[4 marks]**

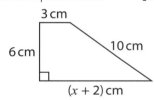

3 cm

6 cm   10 cm

$(x + 2)$ cm

Solution

Area of trapezium = $\frac{1}{2}(a + b)h$

$\frac{1}{2}(3 + x + 2) × 6 = 42$

$3(5 + x) = 42$ since $\frac{1}{2} × 6 = 3$

$15 + 3x = 42$

$3x = 27$

$x = 9$

Perimeter = $6 + 3 + 10 + (9 + 2) = 30$ cm

Worked example

Grade
5

The compound shape is formed by a rectangle and a semicircle.

Work out its area correct to 1 decimal place. **[4 marks]**

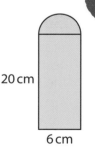

20 cm

6 cm

Solution

Area of rectangle = 20 × 6 = 120 cm²

Radius of semicircle = 3 cm

Area of semicircle = $\pi × 3^2 ÷ 2$ = 14.13... cm²

Total area = 120 + 14.13... = 134.1 cm² (to 1 dp)

Exam corner

Grade
5

The shape of a playground is formed by a rectangle and part of a circle, as shown.

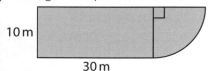

10 m

30 m

Work out

a) the area of the playground **[I got ___/4 marks]**

b) the perimeter of the playground. **[___/3 marks]**

Give both your answers to the nearest integer.

Plans and elevations

You can represent a 3D shape in different ways. Instead of sketching the shape in 3D you can draw a 2D view from a particular direction.

Key points

- A **face** is a flat surface.
- An **edge** is a line where two faces meet.
- A **vertex** (plural **vertices**) is a point where three or more edges meet.
- A **plan** is the view from directly above.
- An **elevation** is the view from the side or front.
- There may be parts you can't see in a 3D sketch of a shape, because they're behind other parts.

Remember this...

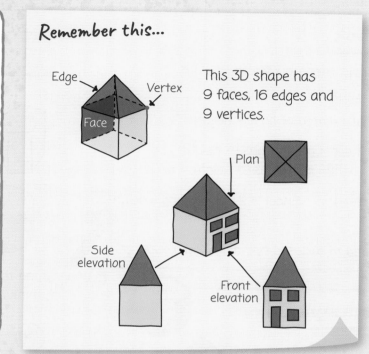

This 3D shape has 9 faces, 16 edges and 9 vertices.

Confidence bar

Sorted!

- [✓]
- [✓]
- [✓]

Had a look

Exam corner

1. The 3D solid is made using six cubes. Draw

   a) the plan

   b) the side elevation

   c) the front elevation.

   [I got ___/3 marks]

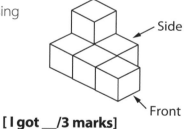

2. The plan view and front and side elevations of a 3D solid are shown on the grid.

Plan	Front elevation	Side elevation

   a) Draw a 3D sketch of the solid.　　[___/2 marks]

   b) Write the number of

      i) vertices

      ii) edges

      iii) faces the solid has.　　[___/3 marks]

Worked example

The 3D solid shown is made using eight cubes.
Draw a plan of the solid on the grid.

[2 marks]

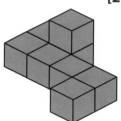

Solution

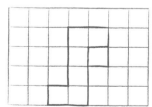

The plan can be drawn in any orientation, as long as it's from above.

Prisms and cylinders

Prisms have a polygon as a base and a constant cross section. A cylinder is like a prism but with a circular base.

Formula box

Volume of a cuboid = length × width × height
= *lwh*

Volume of a prism = area of base × height

Volume of a cylinder = area of base × height
= π × radius² × height = $\pi r^2 h$

Curved surface area of cylinder = 2 × π × radius × height
= $2\pi rh$

Total surface area of a closed cylinder = $2\pi rh + 2\pi r^2$

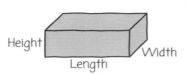

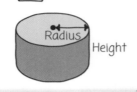

To understand the curved surface area of a cylinder, think of the net of a cylinder:

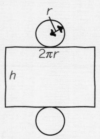

The rectangle will wrap around the circumference, so its width is $C = 2\pi r$

Worked example

Grade 4

Work out the volume of this prism. **[2 marks]**

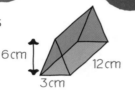

6 cm
12 cm
3 cm

Solution

Area of triangular base = $\frac{1}{2}$ × 3 × 6
= 9 cm²

Volume = 9 × 12 = 108 cm³

Worked example

Grade 5

Work out the surface area of this closed cylinder to 1 dp. **[3 marks]**

3 cm
8 cm

Solution

Curved surface area = 2 × π × 3 × 8 = 48π

Area of circular base = π × 3² = 9π

Total surface area = 48π + 9π + 9π = 207.3 cm²

Examiner's tip!

Take care to avoid a common mistake when finding the surface area – this is not a solid cylinder: it is only closed at one end.

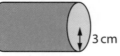

Exam corner

Grade 4

1. The prism shown has a volume of 324 cm³. Work out the length of the sides marked *x* **[I got ___/3 marks]**

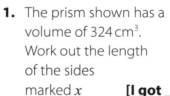
8 cm
x
x

2. A cylindrical tube for sweets is open at one end.
   The diameter of the tube is 6 cm and the length is 20 cm.
   a) Calculate the surface area of the tube in terms of π
      [___/3 marks]

   The tube is made from 2 mm thick cardboard with a density of 0.6 g/cm³.
   b) Calculate the mass of the empty tube to 3 sf.
      [___/3 marks]

Grade 6

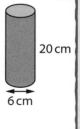
20 cm
6 cm

Spheres and pyramids

A **sphere** is a 'ball-shaped' 3D shape. A **pyramid** has a polygon as the base and all the other faces meet at a vertex.

Formula box

For a sphere with radius r:

Volume of sphere $= \frac{4}{3}\pi r^3$

Surface area of sphere $= 4\pi r^2$

Volume of pyramid $= \frac{1}{3} \times$ area of base $\times$ height

You'll be given the sphere formulae in the exam if you need them.

Learn this! It works for **any** kind of pyramid.

Height
Base

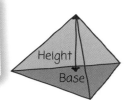

Confidence bar

Sorted!

Had a look

Worked example

Grade 5

A sphere has a surface area of $36\pi\,\text{cm}^2$. Work out the volume of the sphere in terms of π **[4 marks]**

Solution

Surface area is given by $4\pi r^2$, which means that, for this sphere,

$4\pi r^2 = 36\pi$

$\dfrac{4\pi r^2}{4\pi} = \dfrac{36\pi}{4\pi}$ Divide both sides by 4π.

$r^2 = 9$

$r = 3\,\text{cm}$

Now use the formula for volume:

Volume $= \dfrac{4}{3} \times \pi \times 3^3$

$= \dfrac{4}{3} \times \pi \times 27$

$= 36\pi\,\text{cm}^3$ Leave the answer in terms of π

Worked example

Grade 5

The base of a pyramid is a square with side length 9 cm and a height of 23 cm. Work out the volume of the pyramid. **[2 marks]**

23 cm

9 cm

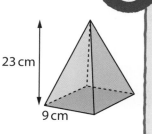

Solution

Volume $= \dfrac{1}{3} \times$ area of base $\times$ height

$= \dfrac{1}{3} \times (9 \times 9) \times 23$

$= 621\,\text{cm}^3$

Examiner's tip!

Always write formulae before you use them.

See page 64 for how to convert between units of volume.

Exam corner

Grade 5

1. A sphere has a radius of 12 cm.

    a) Work out the volume of the sphere. **[I got __/2 marks]**

    b) Work out the surface area of the sphere. **[__/2 marks]**

    Give your answers to 3 significant figures.

A hemisphere is half a sphere.

Grade 6

2. A hemisphere has a radius of 2 m.

    a) Work out the volume of the hemisphere in terms of π 2 m **[__/3 marks]**

    b) Work out the volume of the hemisphere in cm^3, to the nearest whole number. **[__/2 marks]**

Cones and frustums

A **frustum of a cone** is the 3D shape left behind after removing a cone from the top of a larger, similar cone.

Key points

Volume of cone = $\frac{1}{3}$ × area of base × height

$= \frac{1}{3}\pi r^2 h$

Curved surface area of cone = $\pi r l$

Area of base of cone = πr^2

Total surface area of cone = $\pi r l + \pi r^2$

r is the radius of the base

h is the height

l is the slant height

Worked example

Grade 7

A frustum is made by removing the small cone from the larger cone. Work out the volume of the frustum in terms of π **[4 marks]**

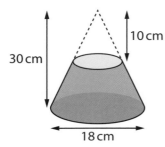

Solution

The smaller cone is similar to the larger cone.

Work out the scale factor: SF = $\frac{10}{30}$ = $\frac{1}{3}$

Radius of larger cone = 18 ÷ 2 = 9 cm

Radius of smaller cone = 9 × $\frac{1}{3}$ = 3 cm

Volume of large cone = $\frac{1}{3}\pi \times 9^2 \times 30 = 810\pi$ cm³

Volume of small cone = $\frac{1}{3}\pi \times 3^2 \times 10 = 30\pi$ cm³

Volume of frustum = $810\pi - 30\pi = 780\pi$ cm³

Worked example

Grade 7

The base of a cone has radius 12 cm. Its volume is 768π cm³. Work out its surface area. **[4 marks]**

Solution

Volume = $\frac{1}{3}\pi \times 12^2 \times h = 768\pi$

$48\pi h = 768\pi$

$h = 16$ cm

Sketch the right-angled triangle inside the cone, then use Pythagoras' theorem:

$l = \sqrt{16^2 + 12^2} = 20$ cm

Curved surface area = $\pi \times r \times l$

$= \pi \times 12 \times 20 = 240\pi$ cm²

Area of base = $\pi \times 12^2 = 144\pi$ cm²

Total surface area = $240\pi + 144\pi$

$= 384\pi$ cm² (≈ 1206 cm²)

Exam corner

Grade 6

1. A cone for chips has dimensions as shown.

   a) Work out the volume of the cone in terms of π

   [I got ___/2 marks]

   b) Work out the area of card needed to make the cone in terms of π **[___/3 marks]**

2. A frustum of a cone has dimensions as shown. Work out its volume. **[___/5 marks]**

Grade 7

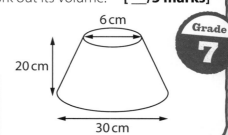

See page 82 for Pythagoras' theorem.

Constructing triangles

You can construct triangles with given side lengths using a ruler and a pair of compasses. 'Construct' means draw accurately.

Key points

You can use a ruler and a protractor to accurately draw a triangle when you know:
- angle-side-angle (ASA) or
- side-angle-side (SAS) or
- hypotenuse and one other side of a right-angled triangle (RHS).

To construct a triangle when you know all three side lengths (SSS), you need a pair of compasses:

STEP 1: Use a ruler to draw the first side.
STEP 2: Set your compasses to the next side length and draw an arc from one vertex.
STEP 3: Set your compasses to the final side length and draw an arc.
STEP 4: Draw lines to the point where the arcs meet to complete the triangle.

> See page 72 for more on congruent triangles.

See page 72 for more on congruent triangles.

Confidence bar

Sorted!

Had a look

Worked example

Construct a triangle with side lengths 7 cm, 4 cm and 5 cm. **[3 marks]**

Solution

Step 2: Set compass to 5cm and draw an arc. Put point of compass here.

(Step 2) (Step 3)

Step 3: Set compass to 4cm and draw an arc. Put compass point here.

Step 1: Use a ruler to draw a horizontal 7cm line.

(Step 4) (Step 4)

(Step 1)

Step 4: Draw lines from the ends of the horizontal line to where the arcs cross, to complete the triangle.

Exam corner

1. Use a ruler and a protractor to draw this parallelogram.

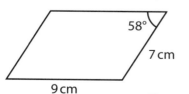

58°
7 cm
9 cm

[I got ___/3 marks]

2. a) Draw a triangle with side lengths 9 cm, 5 cm and 8 cm.
   [___/3 marks]

   b) Construct a 60° angle. **[___/2 marks]**

Examiner's tip!

Do not rub out the arcs. These are called your **construction lines**.

NO ARCS = NO MARKS!

An equilateral triangle has three 60° angles, so here you can construct a triangle like in the worked example, but with all sides the same length.

Perpendiculars and bisectors

You need a compass to construct perpendicular lines and bisectors.

Key points

- **Perpendicular** lines are at 90°.
- The shortest distance from a point to a line is the perpendicular distance.
- A **bisector** cuts a line or an angle exactly in half.
- The **perpendicular bisector** of a line segment cuts the line in half at right angles.

To draw the perpendicular bisector of AB:

STEP 1: Put the point of the compasses at A and draw arcs above and below the line.

STEP 2: Repeat at B

STEP 3: Join up the points where the arcs meet.

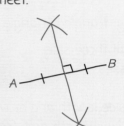

If your arcs don't cross, then your compasses aren't wide enough – ensure they are open wider than halfway.

Worked example

Draw the perpendicular from the dot to the line. **[2 marks]**

Solution

STEP 1: Put point of compasses on the dot and draw two arcs on the line.

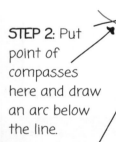

STEP 2: Put point of compasses here and draw an arc below the line.

STEP 3: Repeat on this side – don't change the width of the compasses!

STEP 4: Draw the line from the dot through where the arcs meet.

Worked example

Use compasses to bisect the angle. **[2 marks]**

Solution

STEP 1: Put point of compasses on the vertex and draw an arc on each line.

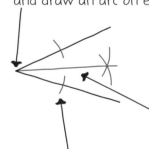

STEP 3: Repeat on the other line, so you have two arcs crossing.

STEP 2: Put point of compasses at this point and draw another arc.

STEP 4: To bisect the angle, draw the line from the vertex to where the arcs meet.

Exam corner

1. Draw the perpendicular of the line *AB* through *P*
   [I got __/2 marks]

2. Draw the angle bisector of angle *AOB*
   [__/2 marks]

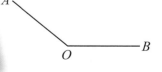

Remember to leave all your construction lines visible.

Loci

A **locus** (plural **loci**) is a set of points that follow a certain rule.

Key points

- The locus of points a fixed distance from a point is a circle.
- The locus of points a fixed distance from a line is a parallel line.
- The locus of points **equidistant** from two points is a perpendicular bisector of the line segment joining those two points.
- The locus of points **equidistant** from two non-parallel lines is an angle bisector of the angle formed where the two lines join.

> Remember this...
> Equidistant means equal distance.

Confidence bar

Sorted!

☑

☑

☑

Had a look

Worked example

Grade 6

A runway is 3 km long. A fence surrounds the runway at a distance of 1.2 km from the runway.

a) Make a scale drawing of the runway, modelled as a line AB, and the fence, using a scale of 1 : 60 000 **[3 marks]**

b) Shade the region where points inside the fence are closer to B than to A **[3 marks]**

Solution

a) Convert 3 km into cm: 3 km = 3000 m = 300 000 cm
Length of AB in drawing = 300 000 ÷ 60 000 = 5 cm
Distance of fence = 1.2 km = 1200 m = 120 000 cm
Distance in drawing = 120 000 ÷ 60 000 = 2 cm

b) Construct the **perpendicular bisector** of the line AB. Shade the region closer to B

> Draw a 5 cm line for the runway. Then draw **parallel lines** 2 cm away and a semicircle of radius 2 cm at each end, for the fence.

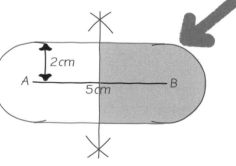

Exam corner

Grade 5

a) Use compasses to draw the locus of points that are equidistant from lines AB and AC **[I got ___/2 marks]**

b) Shade the region that is
- less than 3 cm from point A <u>and</u>
- closer to line AB than to line AC

[___/3 marks]

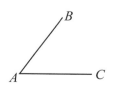

Examiner's tip!

If an exam question tells you to 'draw' then you need to make an accurate representation (not just a sketch).

Pythagoras' theorem

Use Pythagoras' theorem to find missing sides in right-angled triangles.

Grade 4–5

Formula box

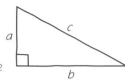

Pythagoras' theorem is:

$$a^2 + b^2 = c^2$$

where c is the **hypotenuse** (longest side) of the triangle and a and b are the other two sides.

Remember these chants...

To find the hypotenuse,

Square–Square–Add–Root

To find another side,

Square–Square–Subtract–Root

Confidence bar

Sorted!

☑
☑
☑

Had a look

Worked example

Grade 4

Work out the missing side lengths in these triangles. **[4 marks]**

a)

7 cm
x
15 cm

b)
3.5 cm
y 9.8 cm

Use your calculator to work these out.

Solution

a) $x^2 = 7^2 + 15^2$

$x = \sqrt{7^2 + 15^2} = 16.6$ cm (to 1 dp)

b) $9.8^2 = 3.5^2 + y^2$

$y^2 = 9.8^2 - 3.5^2$

$y = \sqrt{9.8^2 - 3.5^2} = 9.2$ cm (to 1 dp)

Worked example

The points A and B have coordinates $(1, 2)$ and $(4, -2)$. Work out the length of AB **[3 marks]**

Grade 5

Solution

Plot the points A and B on a coordinate grid.

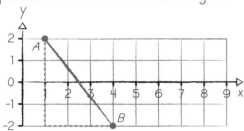

The right-angled triangle has a base of 3 and a height of 4, so $(AB)^2 = 3^2 + 4^2 = 25$

$$AB = \sqrt{25} = 5$$

Exam corner

Grade 4

1. Work out the missing side lengths in these triangles.

Give your answers correct to 1 decimal place. **[I got ___/4 marks]**

a)
14 cm
17 cm
x

b)
y
4.2 cm
7.6 cm

2. Which of these are not the side lengths of a right-angled triangle?

Grade 4

Circle the correct answer.

12 cm, 13 cm, 5 cm   2 cm, 3 cm, 4 cm

8 cm, 10 cm, 6 cm   24 cm, 25 cm, 7 cm   **[___/1 mark]**

Examiner's tip!

If you get a question like this, you need to work out $a^2 + b^2$ and see whether it equals c^2 (where c is the longest side).

CLIMB TO **9** See pages 120–121 for more practice

Trigonometry 1

You can use trigonometry to find the lengths of sides in right-angled triangles.

Grade
5-6

Formula box

You need to learn these ratios for right-angled triangles:

$$\sin\theta = \frac{\text{opposite}}{\text{hypotenuse}}$$

$$\cos\theta = \frac{\text{adjacent}}{\text{hypotenuse}}$$

$$\tan\theta = \frac{\text{opposite}}{\text{adjacent}}$$

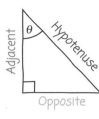

The **hypotenuse** is the longest side.

The opposite is opposite the angle θ.

The adjacent is next to the angle θ.

Remember this...

You can use a mnemonic such as...

Silly Old Harry Chased A Horse Through Our Attic

Or simply:

SOH-CAH-TOA

People normally pronounce this 'sock-ah-toe-ah'.

Worked example

Grade 5

Work out the value of x in this triangle.

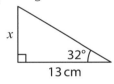

x

32°

13 cm

[2 marks]

Solution

You know the <u>adjacent</u> side is 13 cm, you want to find the <u>opposite</u> side, so use $\tan\theta = \frac{opposite}{adjacent}$

Cover up the O to get T × A:

T | A

$x = \tan 32° × 13$

$= 8.1\,\text{cm}$ (to 1 dp)

Calculator tip

Identify these buttons on your calculator.

sin | cos | tan

Exam corner

Grade 5

1. A plank of wood is propped up against a wall. The plank rests 0.5 m from the base of the wall and makes an angle of 70° with the floor. Work out the length of the plank to the nearest centimetre. **[I got ___/2 marks]**

2. The shape has two right-angled triangles. Work out the value of x Give your answer to 1 decimal place. **[___/3 marks]**

Grade 6

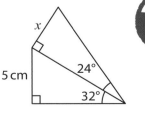

x

5 cm

24°

32°

Examiner's tip!

Draw a diagram to show the situation.

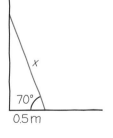

x

70°

0.5 m

Start by calculating the length of the side that is shared by the two triangles.

Trigonometry 2

You can use trigonometry to work out angles in right-angled triangles.

Key points

To find an angle in a right-angled triangle when you know two side lengths:

STEP 1: Identify which two sides you know out of Hypotenuse, Adjacent, or Opposite.

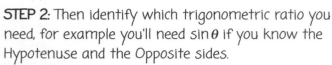

STEP 2: Then identify which trigonometric ratio you need, for example you'll need $\sin\theta$ if you know the Hypotenuse and the Opposite sides.

STEP 3: Set up your equation, $\sin\theta = \dfrac{\text{Opposite}}{\text{Hypotenuse}}$

STEP 4: Rearrange the equation to make θ the subject:

$\theta = \sin^{-1}\dfrac{\text{Opposite}}{\text{Hypotenuse}}$

STEP 5: Use your calculator to find out the inverse sin of this fraction. That gives you the angle θ

Remember this...

SOH-CAH-TOA

Calculator tip

To work out the inverse of cos, sin or tan, you will probably have to press shift or inv first.

$\sin^{-1}$

Confidence bar

Sorted!

☑
☑
☑

Had a look

Worked example

Work out the size of the angle marked x in this triangle.

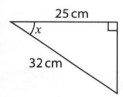

[2 marks]

Solution

You know the <u>adjacent</u> side is 25 cm, and the <u>hypotenuse</u> is 32 cm,

so use $\cos x = \dfrac{\text{opposite}}{\text{hypotenuse}}$

Cover up the C to leave A ÷ H:

$\cos x = \dfrac{25}{32}$

$x = \cos^{-1}\left(\dfrac{25}{32}\right)$

Take the inverse cos of both sides to find x

$= 38.6°$ (to 1 dp)

Examiner's tip!

Get to know your calculator really well before the exam. A lot of students lose marks because they don't know how to use their calculator properly.

Exam corner

1. A tower block is 80 m tall. A camera is placed on the ground 20 m from the base of the tower block.

Work out the angle of elevation of the top of the tower block from the camera, to the nearest degree. **[I got ___/2 marks]**

2. The hypotenuse of a right-angled triangle ABC is three times its height.

Work out the size of $\angle ABC$
Give your answer to the nearest degree. **[___/2 marks]**

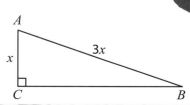

The angle of **elevation** or **depression** is the angle above or below a horizontal line.

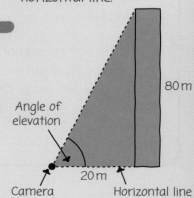

Angle of elevation

80 m

20 m

Camera

Horizontal line

Bearings

Bearings are used in navigation to describe the direction of one object relative to another.

Grade
4-6

Key points

- Bearings are measured CLOCKWISE, starting from NORTH.
- They always have THREE figures, e.g. a bearing of 3° is written as 003°

Remember this...

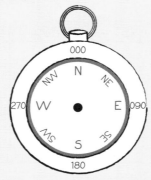

Remember the main compass points:

Never Eat Slimy Worms

Confidence bar

Sorted!

☑
☑
☑

Had a look

Worked example

Grade 6

Alfie leaves his house, walks due east for 10 m and then stops.

a) Write the bearing of Alfie from his house. **[1 mark]**

He then walks 8 m due south and stops again.

b) Work out the new bearing of Alfie from his house. **[3 marks]**

Solution

a) Bearing of Alfie at first stop = 090°

b) $\tan x = \frac{8}{10}$

$x = \tan^{-1}\left(\frac{8}{10}\right) = 39°$ (to nearest degree)

Bearing of Alfie at second stop = 90 + 39
= 129°

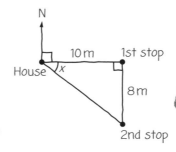

Draw a sketch of the situation to help you understand it. Always remember to draw a line north through the starting point. That's the point from which you want to measure the bearing.

Exam corner

1. Sofia starts at point *A* and walks for 10 m on a bearing of 220° to point *B*. She then walks due north for 5 m to point *C* **Grade 4**

   a) Work out the bearing of *A* from *B* **[I got___/2 marks]**

   b) Make a scale drawing showing points *A*, *B* and *C*
   Use the scale 1 : 50 **[___/3 marks]**

2. A helicopter has flown on a bearing of 290° from an airport for 15 miles. In the same time period, an aeroplane has flown on a bearing of 020° from the airport for 5 miles. Work out the bearing of the aeroplane from the helicopter now. **[___/4 marks]** **Grade 6**

Examiner's tip!

CLIMB TO 9

Always start a bearings question by drawing a sketch. And remember: the bearing of Point *A* from Point *B* will always be 180° different from the bearing of Point *B* from Point *A*

CLIMB TO 9 See pages 126-127 for more practice

Exact values of sin, cos, tan

You need to remember the exact values of the trigonometry functions sin, cos and tan for certain angles.

Key points

Learn these exact values:

θ	0°	30°	45°	60°	90°
$\sin\theta$	0	$\frac{1}{2}$	$\frac{1}{\sqrt{2}}$	$\frac{\sqrt{3}}{2}$	1
$\cos\theta$	1	$\frac{\sqrt{3}}{2}$	$\frac{1}{\sqrt{2}}$	$\frac{1}{2}$	0
$\tan\theta$	0	$\frac{1}{\sqrt{3}}$	1	$\sqrt{3}$	(undefined)

Confidence bar

Sorted!

Had a look

You can use triangles to work out some of these values.

First draw a right-angled isosceles triangle with base and height of 1

Now draw an equilateral triangle with side lengths 2 and split it into two right-angled triangles.

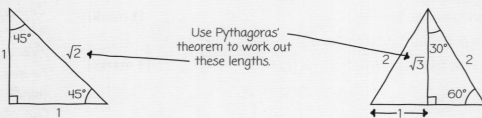

Use Pythagoras' theorem to work out these lengths.

Use SOH–CAH–TOA to write

$\sin 45° = \frac{1}{\sqrt{2}}$ $\cos 45° = \frac{1}{\sqrt{2}}$ $\tan 45° = 1$

$\left(\frac{1}{\sqrt{2}}\text{ can also be written as }\frac{\sqrt{2}}{2}\right)$

Use SOH–CAH–TOA to write

$\sin 30° = \frac{1}{2}$ $\cos 30° = \frac{\sqrt{3}}{2}$ $\tan 30° = \frac{1}{\sqrt{3}}$

$\sin 60° = \frac{\sqrt{3}}{2}$ $\cos 60° = \frac{1}{2}$ $\tan 60° = \sqrt{3}$

Exam corner

Grade 5

1. Work out the value of x
   Circle the correct answer.

   $\sqrt{3}$ $\frac{\sqrt{3}}{2}$ 1 $\frac{2}{\sqrt{3}}$ **[I got ___/1 mark]**

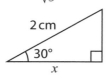

Grade 7

2. Work out the size of angle x

   [___/3 marks]

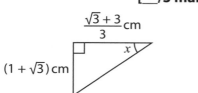

Worked example

Grade 5

Work out the value of x in this triangle.   **[3 marks]**

Solution

You have the <u>opposite</u> side and want to know the <u>hypotenuse</u>, so use $\sin\theta = \dfrac{opposite}{hypotenuse}$

$x = \dfrac{10}{\sin 30°}$

$= \dfrac{10}{\left(\frac{1}{2}\right)}$ since $\sin 30° = \frac{1}{2}$

$= 20\,cm$

Pythagoras' theorem in 3D

You can use Pythagoras' theorem to find lengths in 3D shapes that contain right angles.

Key points

- To find the longest diagonal in a cuboid, use
  $a^2 + b^2 + c^2 = d^2$

  where a, b and c are the dimensions of the cuboid.

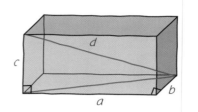

Worked example

Grade 7

Work out the length of BH in this cuboid.

[3 marks]

Solution

Using $a^2 + b^2 + c^2 = d^2$:

$BH^2 = 4^2 + 2^2 + 13^2$

$\quad = 189$

$BH = \sqrt{189}$

$\quad = 13.7\,\text{cm to 1 dp}$

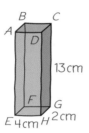

> You can't easily use the formula here. Look for right-angled triangles.

Worked example

Grade 8

The diagram shows a triangular prism. The base ABC is an isosceles triangle. The distance between A and E is 11 cm. Work out the exact length of CB

[3 marks]

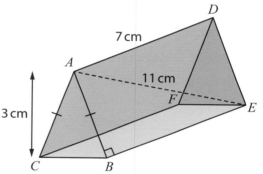

Solution

Consider triangle ABE

$AB^2 = 11^2 - 7^2$

$\quad = 72$

$AB = \sqrt{72}$

Consider triangle AMB

$BM^2 = (\sqrt{72})^2 - 3^2$

$\quad = 63$

$BM = \sqrt{63} = 3\sqrt{7}$

$CB = 2 \times 3\sqrt{7} = 6\sqrt{7}\,\text{cm}$

Exam corner

Grade 7

1. Work out the exact length of the longest diagonal in a cube with side length 4 cm. Give your answer as a surd in its simplest form. **[I got ___/3 marks]**

2. The square base of this pyramid has side length 8 cm.

Grade 8

$AB = AC = AD = AE = 14\,\text{cm}$

Work out the height of the pyramid.

[___/3 marks]

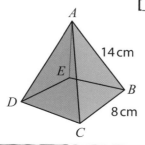

> $AB = AC = AD = AE$ tells you that A is directly above the centre of the square $BCDE$

Trigonometry in 3D

You can use trigonometry to find lengths and angles in 3D shapes that contain right angles.

Key points

- To use trigonometry in 3D shapes, make 2D sketches of the right-angled triangles you are interested in.

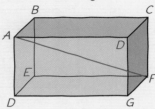

To find the angle *AF* makes with the base *DEFG*:

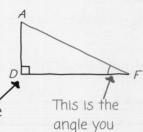

Choose the point on the base that is directly below *A* (to give a right angle).

This is the angle you want.

Worked example

This pyramid has a horizontal rectangular base. The vertex *A* is vertically above *M*, which is the midpoint of *EC*

Work out the size of the angle between *AC* and the base *BCDE*

[5 marks]

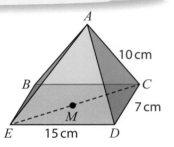

Grade
8

Solution

Consider △*CDE* (right-angled since *BCDE* is a rectangle).

Use Pythagoras' theorem: $EC^2 = 15^2 + 7^2 = 274$
$$EC = \sqrt{274}$$

M is midpoint of *EC*, so $CM = \frac{1}{2}\sqrt{274} = 8.276...$

Consider △*ACM* (right-angled since *A* is vertically above *M*).

Use trigonometry: $\cos x = \dfrac{8.276...}{10}$

$$x = \cos^{-1}\left(\frac{8.276...}{10}\right) = 34.1°$$

Angle between *AC* and base = 34.1° to 1 decimal place

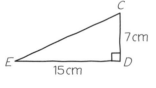

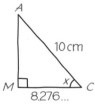

Exam corner

Grade
8

1. The diagram shows a cuboid. Work out the angle *BHF* that *HB* makes with the base *EFGH* **[I got __/4 marks]**

2. The diagram shows a triangular prism. Work out the angle that *DB* makes with the plane *BCFE* **[__/5 marks]**

Grade
8

A plane is a flat surface.

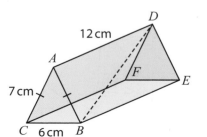

sine and cosine rules

There are two trigonometry rules that work for all triangles, not just right-angled ones: the **sine rule** and the **cosine rule**.

Formula box

sine rule

To find an angle: $\dfrac{\sin A}{a} = \dfrac{\sin B}{b} = \dfrac{\sin C}{c}$

To find a side: $\dfrac{a}{\sin A} = \dfrac{b}{\sin B} = \dfrac{c}{\sin C}$

cosine rule

To find an angle: $\cos A = \dfrac{b^2 + c^2 - a^2}{2bc}$

To find a side: $a^2 = b^2 + c^2 - 2bc \cos A$

Remember, opposite sides and angles have the same letter...

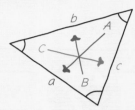

Worked example

Grade 8

Work out the length of AB **[4 marks]**

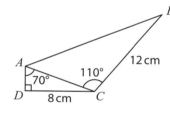

Solution

Consider right-angled triangle ACD:

$\sin 70° = \dfrac{8}{AC}$

$AC = \dfrac{8}{\sin 70°} = 8.51...$

Now look at triangle ABC:

cosine rule gives

$AB^2 = (8.51...)^2 + 12^2 - 2 \times 8.51... \times 12 \times \cos 110°$
$\qquad = 286.36...$

$AB = \sqrt{286.36...} = 16.9$ cm to 1 decimal place

> See page 83 for use of trigonometry in right-angled triangles.

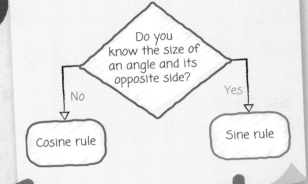

Do you know the size of an angle and its opposite side?

No → Cosine rule

Yes → Sine rule

Worked example

Grade 7

Work out the size of the angle marked x

[3 marks]

Solution

Use the sine rule: $\dfrac{\sin x}{8} = \dfrac{\sin 95°}{12}$

$\sin x = \dfrac{8 \sin 95°}{12} = 0.664...$

$x = 41.6°$ (to 1 d.p.)

Exam corner

Grade 7

Work out the value of x in each of these triangles.

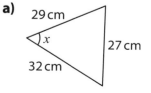

a) 29 cm, x, 27 cm, 32 cm

[I got __/3 marks]

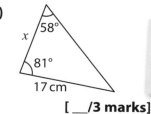

b) 58°, x, 81°, 17 cm

[__/3 marks]

Remember to use the fact that angles sum to 180° to find the third angle in a triangle.

CLIMB TO 9 — See pages 126–127 for more practice

Area of a triangle

You can use trigonometry to work out the area of any triangle.

Formula box

Area of a triangle $= \frac{1}{2}ab\sin C$

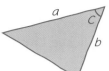

where C is the angle between sides a and b

Worked example

Grade 7

Work out the area of the triangle.

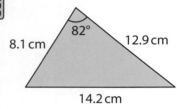

82°
8.1 cm
12.9 cm
14.2 cm

[2 marks]

Solution

Use the two sides that the marked angle is between:

Area $= \frac{1}{2} \times 8.1 \times 12.9 \times \sin 82°$

$= 51.7 \text{ cm}^2$ to 1 decimal place

See page 89 for the sine and cosine rules.

Worked example

The area of triangle ABC is 128 cm^2.

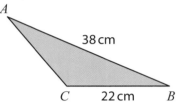

A
38 cm
C 22 cm B

Work out the length of AC **[5 marks]**

Grade 8

Solution

Area $= \frac{1}{2} \times 22 \times 38 \sin(\angle ABC) = 128$

$\sin(\angle ABC) = \dfrac{128}{\frac{1}{2} \times 22 \times 38} = 0.306...$

$\angle ABC = \sin^{-1}(0.306...) = 17.8...°$

Use the cosine rule to find AC:

$AC^2 = 22^2 + 38^2 - 2 \times 22 \times 38 \times \cos(17.8...)$

$= 336.3...$

$AC = \sqrt{336.3...} = 18.3 \text{ cm}$ to 1 decimal place

Exam corner

Grade 7

1. Work out the area of the triangle.

31.6 cm   98°
49°
43.8 cm

[I got ___/2 marks]

2. Work out the area of the triangle.

Grade 8

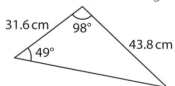

18 cm
15 cm
17 cm

[___/4 marks]

Examiner's tip!

Ensure you are using the correct sides and angles – remember, opposite sides and angles have the same letter in the formulae.

You may need to use the sine rule or the cosine rule to find a side or angle before you can work out the area.

Sectors, arcs & segments

A **sector** is a fraction of the area of a circle. An **arc** is a fraction of the circumference of a circle. A chord splits a circle into two **segments**.

Formula box

If you have a sector of angle θ and radius r:

Area of sector $= \dfrac{\theta}{360} \times$ area of whole circle

$= \dfrac{\theta}{360} \times \pi r^2$

Arc length $= \dfrac{\theta}{360} \times$ circumference of circle

$= \dfrac{\theta}{360} \times 2\pi r$

A sector is the shape of a slice of cake.

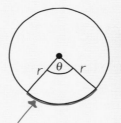

An arc is the curved edge of the slice

Confidence bar

Sorted!

Had a look

Worked example

Grade 6

A circle of radius r has a sector of angle 200° cut from it.

A sector can be bigger than a semicircle.

The perimeter of the sector is 30 cm.
Work out the value of r to 1 decimal place.

[4 marks]

Solution

Perimeter of sector = arc length + 2r

$\dfrac{200}{360} \times 2\pi r + 2r = 30$

$\dfrac{10}{9}\pi r + 2r = 30$

$\left(\dfrac{10}{9}\pi + 2\right)r = 30$

$r = \dfrac{30}{\dfrac{10}{9}\pi + 2} = 5.5\text{ cm to 1 decimal place}$

Worked example

Grade 8

Work out the area of the coloured segment.

[4 marks]

110°

8 cm

Solution

Area of sector $= \dfrac{110}{360} \times \pi \times 8^2$

$= 61.43...\text{ cm}^2$

Area of triangle $= \dfrac{1}{2} \times 8 \times 8 \times \sin 110°$

$= 30.07...\text{ cm}^2$

Area of segment

= area of sector – area of triangle

= 61.43... – 30.07...

= 31.4 cm² to 1 decimal place

Exam corner

Grade 5

1. A circle of radius 9 cm has a sector of angle 35° cut from it. Work out, to 1 decimal place,

9 cm

35°

a) the area   **b)** the arc length
c) the perimeter of the sector.   **[I got ___/6 marks]**

Grade 8

2. Work out the area of the shaded segment.

200°

7 cm

[___/4 marks]

Vectors 1

A **vector** has a size and a direction. There are different ways of writing vectors that you need to know about.

Key points

- The top vector can be written $\overrightarrow{AB}$ as it starts at point A and ends at point B
- It can also be printed in bold type **a**. In handwriting, you would write it with an underline, a
- The **size and direction** of a vector matter, but **not** the position. So, the vector $\overrightarrow{CD}$ is also **a** as it has the same size and direction as the vector $\overrightarrow{AB}$
- The vector **–a** is the same size as **a** and parallel to **a** but in the opposite direction.
- A vector that is parallel to **a** but a different length will be a multiple of **a** such as 2**a**
- To add column vectors, add the top values then add the bottom values.
- To multiply a column vector by a number, multiply both the top and bottom values by the number.

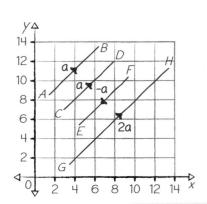

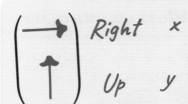

Worked example

Given that $\mathbf{a} = \begin{pmatrix} 4 \\ -2 \end{pmatrix}$ and $\mathbf{b} = \begin{pmatrix} -5 \\ 0 \end{pmatrix}$,

a) work out the column vector 2**b** – **a**   **[1 mark]**
b) show the vectors **a**, **b** and **a** + **b** on a square grid.   **[3 marks]**

Solution

a) $2\underline{b} - \underline{a} = 2\begin{pmatrix} -5 \\ 0 \end{pmatrix} - \begin{pmatrix} 4 \\ -2 \end{pmatrix}$

$= \begin{pmatrix} -10 \\ 0 \end{pmatrix} - \begin{pmatrix} 4 \\ -2 \end{pmatrix}$

$= \begin{pmatrix} -14 \\ 2 \end{pmatrix}$

b)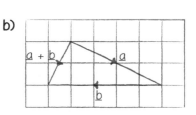

Worked example

$OABC$ is a parallelogram. $\overrightarrow{OA} = \mathbf{a}$ and $\overrightarrow{OC} = \mathbf{c}$

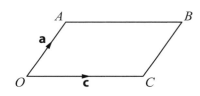

Write these vectors in terms of **a** and **c**

a) $\overrightarrow{CO}$ b) $\overrightarrow{OB}$ **[2 marks]**

Solution

a) $\overrightarrow{CO} = -\underline{c}$ It's parallel to $\overrightarrow{OC}$ but in the opposite direction.

b) $\overrightarrow{OB} = \overrightarrow{OA} + \overrightarrow{AB} = \underline{a} + \underline{c}$

When you write the vectors nose to tail, these letters will always match.

Exam corner

$ABCD$ is a parallelogram.

$\overrightarrow{CD} = \begin{pmatrix} -2 \\ -5 \end{pmatrix}, \overrightarrow{AD} = \begin{pmatrix} 3 \\ -1 \end{pmatrix}$

Work out $\overrightarrow{AC}$ as a column vector.

Circle the correct answer.

$\begin{pmatrix} 5 \\ 4 \end{pmatrix}$ $\begin{pmatrix} -5 \\ -4 \end{pmatrix}$ $\begin{pmatrix} 1 \\ -6 \end{pmatrix}$ $\begin{pmatrix} -1 \\ 6 \end{pmatrix}$ **[I got___/1 mark]**

Vectors 2

You can find vectors involving the midpoints of lines, or even use ratios with vectors.

Key points

- If M is the midpoint of AB,
  Then $\overrightarrow{AM} = \frac{1}{2}\overrightarrow{AB}$

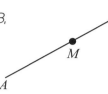

- If vectors **a** and **b** are parallel, then **a** = k**b** (where k is a constant).

Confidence bar

Sorted!

Had a look

Worked example — Grade 6

In the diagram, the point M is the midpoint of AB

Work out $\overrightarrow{OM}$ in terms of vectors **a** and **b**   **[3 marks]**

Solution

$\overrightarrow{OM} = \overrightarrow{OA} + \overrightarrow{AM}$

$= \overrightarrow{OA} + \frac{1}{2}\overrightarrow{AB}$ since M is the midpoint of AB

$= \underline{a} + \frac{1}{2}(-\underline{a} + \underline{b}) = \underline{a} - \frac{1}{2}\underline{a} + \frac{1}{2}\underline{b}$

$= \frac{1}{2}\underline{a} + \frac{1}{2}\underline{b}$

Worked example — Grade 8

$ABCD$ is a trapezium. $\overrightarrow{AB} = 2\overrightarrow{DC}$ and $\overrightarrow{AF} = 2\overrightarrow{AB}$.
E is a point on $\overrightarrow{BC}$ such that $\overrightarrow{CE}:\overrightarrow{EB} = 1:2$

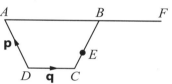

Show that DEF is a straight line.   **[4 marks]**

Solution

$\overrightarrow{DE} = \overrightarrow{DC} + \frac{1}{3}\overrightarrow{CB}$ since $CE:EB = 1:2$

$= \underline{q} + \frac{1}{3}(-\underline{q} + \underline{p} + 2\underline{q})$ since $\overrightarrow{AB} = 2\overrightarrow{DC} = 2\underline{q}$

$= \frac{1}{3}\underline{p} + \frac{4}{3}\underline{q}$

$\overrightarrow{DF} = \overrightarrow{DA} + 2\overrightarrow{AB}$ since $\overrightarrow{AF} = 2\overrightarrow{AB}$

$= \underline{p} + 2(2\underline{q}) = \underline{p} + 4\underline{q} = 3\overrightarrow{DE}$

Therefore, DEF is a straight line.

To show that points A, B and C lie on a straight line, you need to show that any two of AB, AC or BC are multiples of each other.

Exam corner — Grade 8

$\overrightarrow{OA} = $ **a**, $\overrightarrow{OB} = $ **b** and $\overrightarrow{OC} = k$**b**

M is the midpoint of AB
N splits OA in the ratio $5:1$

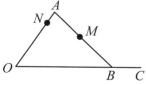

a) Show that $\overrightarrow{NM} = -\frac{1}{3}$**a** $+ \frac{1}{2}$**b**

[I got ___/3 marks]

b) Work out the value of k, given that NMC is a straight line.   **[___/3 marks]**

Use the coefficients of **a** to work out what you must multiply $\overrightarrow{NC}$ by to get $\overrightarrow{NM}$. Then use this information to find the value of k

Sampling

Instead of gathering information from every member of a population, it's sometimes better to use a smaller set of members, called a **sample**.

Key points

- Data from a sample can be used to estimate properties of the whole population.
- The larger the sample, the more accurate the estimates.
- Each member of the population should have an equal chance of being in the sample, otherwise the sample will be **biased**.
- A biased sample will not represent the population well.

Types of data you need to know about:

Quantitative = numerical
  like quantity (a number or amount)

Qualitative = non-numerical
like quality (a characteristic, such as colour)

Primary = data you collect yourself (you are the first person to see it)

Secondary = data someone else has collected (you are at least the second person to see it)

Exam corner

Grade 5

Aston is researching a holiday location and wants to find out about the amount of rain there. He randomly selects 20 of the 48 days of the previous summer holiday and looks online at the weather on those days. The data is in the table.

Type of rain	Number of days
Heavy rain	2
Light rain	5
No rain	13

a) Is this primary or secondary data? Give a reason for your answer. **[I got __/1 mark]**

b) Estimate how many of the 48 days of the summer holiday had light rain. **[__/2 marks]**

c) How could Aston change his sample in order to improve his estimate? **[__/1 mark]**

Worked example

Grade 5

Jessica wants to know how many books students in her school read per month. There are 1000 students in her school, so she wants to use a sample. She decides to go to the library and ask students how many books they have read that month.

a) What type of data will Jessica have? **[2 marks]**

b) Jessica asks 10 students in total, and finds that 2 of them have read more than 5 books that month.
Use this data to estimate how many students in the entire school have read more than 5 books that month. **[2 marks]**

c) Give a reason why the sample might be biased and your estimate in part **b** may not be accurate. **[2 marks]**

Solution

a) This is quantitative primary data (it is numerical and Jessica has collected it herself).

b) $\frac{2}{10} = \frac{1}{5}$ of the students have read more than 5 books

Work out the proportion in the sample who have read more than 5 books.

$\frac{1}{5} \times 1000 = 200$ students

Multiply the proportion in the sample by the total number of students.

c) Not all students in the school have an equal chance of being in the sample, and students in the library are likely to have read more books than average.

Averages and spread

There are three types of average you need to be able to work out: **mean**, **median** and **mode**. The spread of data can be measured using the **range**.

Key points

Mean: Add up all the values and divide by the total number of values.

Median: List the data in order and select the middle value. If there are two middle values, find the number half-way between them.

Mode: The most commonly occurring value. There may be more than one mode, or no mode at all.

Range: The difference between the largest and smallest values.

Mean, median or mode?

– If you have non-numerical data, use **the mode**.

– If the data has an **outlier** (an unusually large or small value), it might be better to use **the median** than the mean. The mean is affected by outliers but the median isn't.

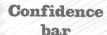

Worked example

Grade 4

The table shows the number of sunny days per week over 21 weeks.

No. of sunny days per week	0	1	2	3	4	5	6	7
Frequency	3	8	4	2	1	1	0	2

Work out

a) the median **[2 marks]**
b) the mode **[1 mark]**
c) the mean **[3 marks]**
d) the range **[1 mark]**

Solution

a) There are 21 values, so the median is the 11th value. Median = 1

b) Mode = 1 (it has the highest frequency)

c) Add a row to the frequency table for number of days × frequency:

No. of sunny days, n	0	1	2	3	4	5	6	7	Total
Frequency, f	3	8	4	2	1	1	0	2	21
$n \times f$	0	8	8	6	4	5	0	14	45

Mean = 45 ÷ 21 = 2.142... = 2.1 (to 1 dp)

d) Range = 7 − 0 = 7

> For mean remember MAD...
> To calculate the mean from a frequency table...
> Multiply each value by its frequency.
> Add up these values.
> Divide by the total number of values.

Exam corner

1. The number of items in the baskets of 20 customers is recorded at a self-service checkout. Work out these values:

No. of items per basket	3	4	5	6	7	8
Frequency	1	5	4	7	2	1

a) median **[I got __/2 marks]**   b) mode **[__/1 mark]**
c) mean **[__/3 marks]**   d) range **[__/1 mark]**

2. A student records the number of items of homework they complete each day for two weeks, and displays the information in a bar chart. Work out the mean. **[__/3 marks]**

Examiner's tip!

Grade 4

First summarise the data in a frequency table.

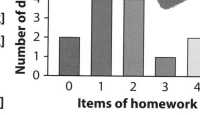

Grade 5

Grouped data

If you have data that has been grouped, you can still estimate the mean and find the **median class** and **modal class**.

Key points

Median class: The group that the middle value lies in.

Modal class: The group with the highest frequency.

To estimate the mean from a grouped frequency table...

Multiply the midpoint of each class by its frequency.

Add up these values.

Divide by the total number of values.

To estimate ... remember MAD...

Worked example

Grade
5

The lengths of 25 pieces of string are recorded in the table.

Length of string (s cm)	Number of pieces of string
$0 < s \le 8$	12
$8 < s \le 12$	6
$12 < s \le 20$	7

a) Write the modal class. **[1 mark]**

b) Work out which class the median lies in. **[2 marks]**

c) Work out an estimate for the mean. **[3 marks]**

This column, although it's got a different heading, shows the frequencies for each class. You could change the heading to 'Frequency'.

Solution

a) $0 < s \le 8$ is the modal class (it has the highest frequency, 12).

b) There are 25 pieces of string so the median will be the 13th.

You could add a running total column to the table:

Length of string (s cm)	Frequency	Running total
$0 < s \le 8$	12	12
$8 < s \le 12$	6	18
$12 < s \le 20$	7	25

13 lies between 12 and 18, so the 13th value lies in the $8 < s \le 12$ class.

c) Add columns for the midpoint and midpoint × frequency:

Length of string (s cm)	Midpoint	Frequency	Midpoint × frequency
$0 < s \le 8$	4	12	48
$8 < s \le 12$	10	6	60
$12 < s \le 20$	16	7	112
Totals		25	220

Estimate for mean = 220 ÷ 25 = 8.8 cm

Remember MAD

Exam corner

Grade
5

The grouped frequency table shows the time per day spent playing computer games by a group of children.

Time (t mins)	Frequency
$0 \le t < 20$	35
$20 \le t < 40$	20
$40 \le t < 60$	16
$60 \le t < 80$	9

a) Write the modal class. **[I got __/1 mark]**

b) Which is the median class? **[__/2 marks]**

c) Work out an estimate for the mean. **[__/3 marks]**

Interquartile range

Another measure of the spread of data is the **interquartile range**. This is the range of the middle 50% of values.

You also need to know about stem-and-leaf diagrams, which are another way of displaying frequencies.

Key points

For data in ascending order:

- The **lower quartile** (Q_1) is the value 25% of the way through the data.
- The **median** (Q_2) is the value 50% of the way through the data.
- The **upper quartile** (Q_3) is the value 75% of the way through the data.
- **Interquartile range** = upper quartile – lower quartile

Worked example

Grade 6

Daisy played 11 games of football. Here are the number of goals she scored in each:
1   0   1   2   0   0   3   1   1   0   2

a) Work out the interquartile range. **[3 marks]**

Jessie also played 11 games of football. Her median number of goals scored was 2 and her interquartile range was 3

b) Compare Daisy's and Jessie's results. **[2 marks]**

Solution

a) Arrange the 11 items of data in ascending order:

0, 0, 0, 0, 1, 1, 1, 1, 2, 2, 3

The position of the lower quartile is $\frac{1}{4}(n + 1) = 3 \Rightarrow$ 3rd value is 0

The position of the upper quartile is $\frac{3}{4}(n + 1) = 9 \Rightarrow$ 9th value is 2

Interquartile range = 2 – 0 = 2 goals

b) The position of the median is $\frac{1}{2}(n + 1) = 6 \Rightarrow$ 6th value is 1

Therefore, Daisy's median number of goals scored is 1

Jessie's median is higher than Daisy's, so Jessie scores more goals on average.

Daisy's interquartile range is smaller than Jessie's, so Daisy scores more consistently.

> Use these rules to work out the position of the quartiles. For n items of data:
>
> Q_1: $\frac{1}{4}(n + 1)$
>
> Q_2: $\frac{1}{2}(n + 1)$
>
> Q_3: $\frac{3}{4}(n + 1)$

Exam corner

Grade 6

This stem-and-leaf diagram shows the number of minutes spent on homework per day by 15 students:

0	3, 8, 9
1	2, 4, 5, 5, 7
2	5, 7, 7, 7
3	3, 5
4	9

Key:

2 | 5 means 25

Work out
- **a)** the mean **[I got __/2 marks]**
- **b)** the median **[__/1 mark]**
- **c)** the interquartile range **[__/3 marks]**

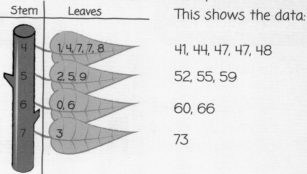

A **stem-and-leaf diagram** displays data in order:

Stem	Leaves	This shows the data:
4	1, 4, 7, 7, 8	41, 44, 47, 47, 48
5	2, 5, 9	52, 55, 59
6	0, 6	60, 66
7	3	73

Key: 4 | 1 means 41

Here, the stem is the tens digits and the leaves are the units digits, but you can have other place values. You must give a key.

Simple charts

You can represent data using simple charts such as pie charts, bar charts (or vertical line charts) and frequency polygons.

Key points

- **Pie charts** show the proportion of the total in each category, so be careful when comparing two pie charts with different totals.
- **Bar charts** should have spaced bars of equal width.
- **Frequency polygons** represent grouped data. Plot the frequency of each class against its **midpoint**, then join with straight lines.

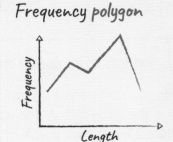

Frequency polygon

Use a ruler for the lines.

Confidence bar

Sorted! ☑ ☑ ☑

Had a look

Worked example

The grouped frequency table shows the heights of a sample of daisies.

Height of daisies (x cm)	Frequency
$2 < x \le 6$	2
$6 < x \le 10$	8
$10 < x \le 14$	24
$14 < x \le 18$	4

a) Amy draws a pie chart to represent the data. She says that the sector for daisies with heights greater than 6 cm and less than or equal to 10 cm should be approximately 76°. Is Amy correct? Show your working. **[2 marks]**

b) James draws a bar chart to represent the data. What does the height of each bar in his bar chart represent? **[1 mark]**

c) Draw a frequency polygon to represent the data in the table. **[3 marks]**

d) Estimate the mean height. **[3 marks]**

Solution

a) Total frequency = 2 + 8 + 24 + 4 = 38

Size of angle = $\frac{8}{38} \times 360 = 75.78...$
= 76° (to nearest degree)

Therefore, Amy is correct.

b) The height of each bar represents the frequency for that class.

c) Plot each frequency against the midpoint of each class. For example, the midpoint of the first class is 4 cm.

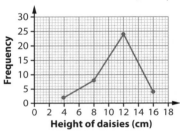

Remember to join the points with straight lines.

d) Total of heights = (4 × 2) + (8 × 8) + (12 × 24) + (16 × 4)
= 424

Mean ≈ 424 ÷ 38 = 11.2 cm (to 1 dp)

Exam corner

1. The dual bar chart shows the number of different flavoured ice creams bought for children and

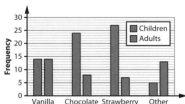

adults. A pie chart is to be drawn to represent the flavours of ice cream bought for children.

a) Work out the angle of the sector to represent vanilla. **[I got __/2 marks]**

A second pie chart is to be drawn the represent the flavours of ice cream bought for adults.

b) Give a reason why the angle of the sector for vanilla will be bigger in the second pie chart. **[__/2 marks]**

2. Draw a frequency polygon to represent the data in the table. **[__/3 marks]**

Height (x cm)	Frequency
$0 < x \le 5$	4
$5 < x \le 10$	12
$10 < x \le 15$	11
$15 < x \le 20$	1

Scatter graphs

A **scatter graph** can be used to see the relationship between two sets of data.

Key points

- If most of the points on a scatter graph lie close to a straight line, there is a **correlation** between the data.
- An **outlier** is a point that doesn't follow the trend of most of the data.
- Zero correlation doesn't necessarily imply no relationship, just no linear correlation.

Positive correlation
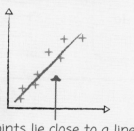
Points lie close to a line with **positive** gradient.

No correlation
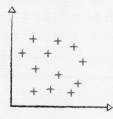
Points are randomly scattered.

Negative correlation
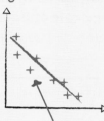
Points lie close to a line with **negative** gradient.

> See page 17 for more on gradients of straight lines.

Worked example

The scatter graph shows the relationship between the age of a person and the speed of texting.

a) Describe the correlation shown and describe what this means in context. **[2 marks]**

b) Identify an outlier and give two possible reasons for it. **[2 marks]**

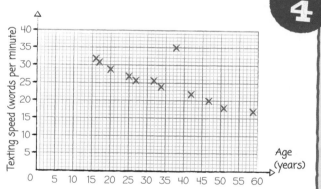

Solution

a) Negative correlation: the older a person is, the slower their speed of texting.

b) $(37\frac{1}{2}, 35)$ is an outlier. It could be a plotting error or there could be a 37-year-old who is very fast at texting.

Exam corner

1. In the worked example, the data point (5, 60) was originally plotted but then removed. Give a reason why this data point may have been removed. **[I got ___/1 mark]**

2. The scatter graph shows the relationship between two variables, x and y

a) Give a reason why the diagram does not show positive correlation. **[___/1 mark]**

Sara claims that there is no relationship between x and y

b) Comment on Sara's claim. **[___/1 mark]**

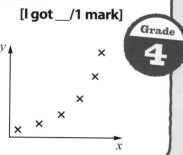

Lines of best fit

If two sets of data are correlated, you can draw a line of best fit on the scatter graph and use it to make estimations.

Key points

- A **line of best fit** should follow the trend of the data, ignoring any outliers.
- **Interpolating** means using a line of best fit to estimate a value within the range of the data. This will be a reliable estimate.
- **Extrapolating** means extending the line of best fit to estimate a value outside the range of the data. This estimate might be unreliable.
- **Correlation does not necessarily indicate causation.** If two sets of data appear to be correlated, it doesn't mean that a change in one <u>causes</u> a change in the other.

Worked example

Grade 5

This question refers to the scatter graph from page 99

a) Estimate the speed of texting for a 40-year-old.
[2 marks]

Millie claims that the graph shows that a 5-year-old will be able to text approximately 34 words per minute.

b) Comment on Millie's claim. **[1 mark]**

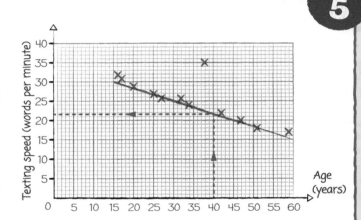

Solution

a) Ignore the outlier and draw a line of best fit. Draw a line from 40 to the line of best fit. The line gives an estimate of 22 words/minute.

b) You don't have any data for people under 16, so Millie is using extrapolation and her estimate is unreliable (and seems unlikely).

Exam corner

Grade 5

The scatter diagram shows the relationship between the outside temperature and the cost per day of heating a building.

a) Describe the correlation shown. **[I got __/1 mark]**

b) Draw a line of best fit and use it to estimate the cost of heating the building when the outside temperature is 7 °C. **[__/2 marks]**

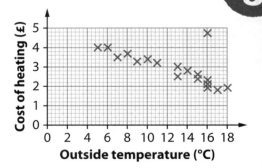

c) Estimate the increase in the cost of heating per 1 °C decrease in temperature. **[__/2 marks]**

d) Give a reason why your line of best fit shouldn't be used to estimate the cost of heating the building when the outside temperature is 0 °C. **[__/1 mark]**

Time series

Grade 4

A **time series graph** is a line graph that shows how data changes over time.

Worked example

Grade 4

Prisha is revising for her Maths GCSE. She does a practice paper every month and records her score in the table.

Month	Sept	Oct	Nov	Dec	Jan	Feb	Mar	Apr
Score (%)	44	48	42	50	55	62	65	70

a) Draw a time series graph for this data. **[3 marks]**

b) Describe the trend of the data and identify any outliers. **[2 marks]**

Confidence bar

Sorted! ☑

☑

☑

Had a look

Solution

a) Plot each of the points then use a ruler to join with straight lines.

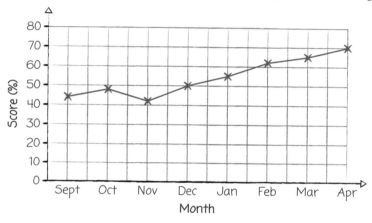

To draw a time series graph...
- put time on the x-axis
- put the thing being measured on the y-axis
- plot the points then join them with straight lines.

b) The general trend of score is increasing, apart from a dip in November (that score is an outlier).

Exam corner

Grade 4

The average cost of British strawberries over a 3-year period, during spring, summer and autumn, is shown in the time series graph.

a) Describe the general trend.
[I got ___/1 mark]

b) In which season are British strawberries cheapest? **[___/1 mark]**

c) Work out the mean price of 1 kg of British strawberries over the three seasons shown for 2019
[___/2 marks]

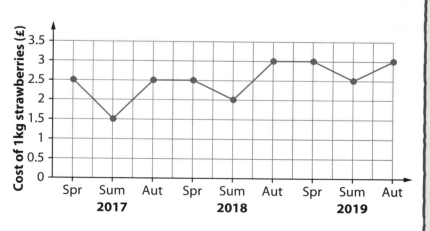

Box plots

A **box plot** can be used to show the median, range and interquartile range of data and is useful for comparing sets of data.

Features of a box plot:

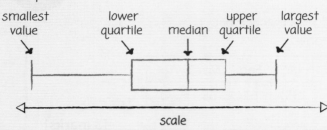

smallest value · lower quartile · median · upper quartile · largest value

scale

Worked example

The heights of a group of children are given (in cm):

144   125   141   147   135   136   132   142   133

Represent this data using a box plot. **[4 marks]**

Solution

Re-order the heights:

125   132   133   135   136   141   142   144   147

There are 9 children.

Median = 5th value = 136 cm

To find the quartiles: $\frac{1}{4}(9 + 1) = 2.5$ and $\frac{3}{4}(9 + 1) = 7.5$

Lower quartile = mean of 2nd and 3rd values = 132.5 cm

Upper quartile = mean of 7th and 8th values = 143 cm

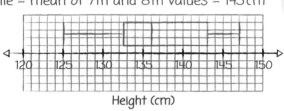

Height (cm)

> A value of 2.5 here means you need the mean of the 2nd and 3rd values.

See page 97 for more on finding quartiles.

Examiner's tip!

If you are told to compare two sets of data, make at least one comparison of an average (mean, median or mode) and one comparison of the spread (range or interquartile range). Make sure you use the correct mathematical terms.

Exam corner

A group of 19 GCSE students were asked how many pieces of homework they currently have to complete. The results are in the table below.

Number of pieces of homework	Frequency
2	1
3	2
4	4
5	5
6	5
7	2

a) Draw a box plot to represent this information.

[I got __/4 marks]

A group of year 7 students were asked the same question. The results are summarised in this box plot.

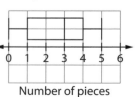

Number of pieces of homework

b) Complete this sentence.

25% of year 7 students have at least .... pieces of homework. **[__/1 mark]**

c) Compare the results for year 7 and GCSE students. **[__/2 marks]**

Cumulative frequency

A **cumulative frequency** graph shows the total frequency up to each point and can be used to estimate the median and quartiles.

Key points

- In a **cumulative frequency** graph, you plot the **running total** of the frequency against the end point of each class.
- Join the points with a smooth curve.
- To estimate the median, draw a line across at 50% of the total frequency.
- To estimate the lower and upper quartiles, draw lines across at 25% and 75% of the total frequency.

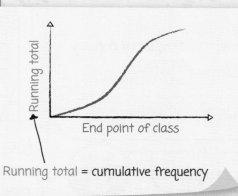

Running total = cumulative frequency

Worked example

The cumulative frequency graph shows the height of some horses.

Estimate

a) the median height   **[1 mark]**

b) the interquartile range   **[3 marks]**

c) the percentage of horses measuring less than 2.4 m.   **[2 marks]**

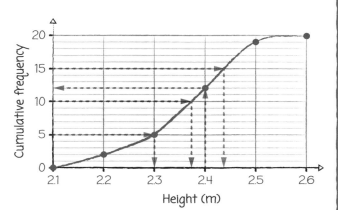

Solution

a) There are 20 horses in total, so for the median, draw a line across at 10
Median ≈ 2.37 m

b) For the lower and upper quartiles, draw lines across at 5 and 15
Lower quartile ≈ 2.30 m, upper quartile ≈ 2.44 m
Interquartile range ≈ 2.44 − 2.30 = 0.14 m

c) Draw a line up from 2.4 m. This gives 12 horses, which is 60% of 20

Exam corner

The table shows the duration of a sample of podcasts.

a) Draw a cumulative frequency graph to represent this data.   **[I got __/3 marks]**

b) Use your graph to estimate

   i) the median   **[__/1 mark]**

   ii) the interquartile range.   **[__/2 marks]**

c) Work out the upper and lower bounds for the range of the sample.   **[__/2 marks]**

Duration (d mins)	Frequency
$0 < d \le 5$	1
$5 < d \le 10$	2
$10 < d \le 15$	4
$15 < d \le 20$	12
$20 < d \le 25$	7
$25 < d \le 30$	2

Start by adding a 'running total' or 'cumulative frequency' column to the table.

Histograms

Histograms can be used to represent grouped data. They are particularly useful when the class widths are different.

Key points

In a histogram,

- the y-axis shows the **frequency density**
- frequency density = $\frac{\text{frequency}}{\text{class width}}$
- the **area** of a bar is proportional to the frequency of the class.

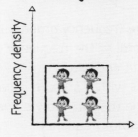

Bar chart   vs   Histogram

Height represents frequency

Area represents frequency

Worked example

The histogram shows the times that some children took to complete a short test.

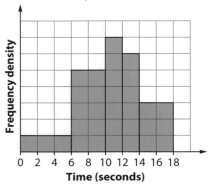

Time (seconds)

Three children completed the test in under 6 s.

a) Work out the number of children that took between 6 s and 10 s to complete the test. **[2 marks]**

b) Estimate the number of children that took more than 13 s to complete the test. **[2 marks]**

c) Give a reason why your answer to part **b** is only an estimate. **[1 mark]**

Solution

a) Using the information that 3 children completed the test in under 6 s, you can see that each square on the histogram represents 1 child.
10 children took between 6 s and 10 s.

b) You need all of the 14–18 class (6 children) and half of the 12–14 class (3 children).
An estimated 9 children took more than 13 s.

c) It was assumed that the times are equally spaced between 12 s and 14 s (so that half of these children took more than 13 s).

Exam corner

1. The incomplete histogram and table show information about the mass of some pigs.

Mass (*m* kg)	Frequency
$50 \leq m < 100$	5
$100 \leq m < 200$	
$200 \leq m < 300$	30
$300 \leq m < 500$	

Use the data for the first bar to work out the scale for the frequency density.

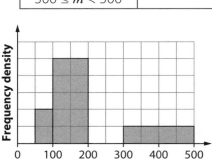

Mass (kg)

Complete the table and the histogram. **[I got ___ /4 marks]**

 2. a) Use the histogram in the worked example to estimate the mean time taken to complete the test. **[___ /4 marks]**

b) What assumption did you make in your calculation to part **a**? **[___ /1 mark]**

Multiply the midpoint of each bar in the histogram by the frequency (represented by the area of each bar). Add these together and divide by the total frequency.

Theoretical probability

A **probability** tells you how likely an event is to happen.

Key points

- Probabilities are always **between 0 and 1**
- If all outcomes of an experiment are **equally likely**, then:

$$\text{Probability of an event happening} = \frac{\text{number of ways it can happen}}{\text{total number of possible outcomes}}$$

- This value is called the **theoretical probability** of the event, written **P(event)**.
- A probability can be expressed as a fraction, a decimal or a percentage.
- The probabilities of all possible **mutually exclusive** outcomes of an experiment must add up to 1:

$$\text{P(event happening)} = 1 - \text{P(event not happening)}$$

Confidence bar

Sorted!

☑
☑
☑

Had a look

See pages 112 and 113 for more on Venn diagrams.

Mutually exclusive events can't happen together.

Odd numbers   Even numbers

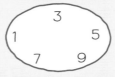   

A number cannot be both odd and even.

Worked example

Each card in a pack of cards shows a shape that may be a triangle, a square, a pentagon or a hexagon.

The table shows the probabilities of selecting a triangle or a square.

Shape	Triangle	Square	Pentagon	Hexagon
Probability	0.38	0.26		

The ratio of pentagons to hexagons in the pack is 5 : 7

Complete the table. **[2 marks]**

Solution

The four probabilities must add up to 1

$1 - (0.38 + 0.26) = 0.36$

$\text{P(pentagon)} : \text{P(hexagon)} = 5 : 7$

$\text{P(pentagon)} = \frac{5}{12} \text{ of } 0.36 = 0.15$

$\text{P(hexagon)} = \frac{7}{12} \text{ of } 0.36 = 0.21$

Shape	Triangle	Square	Pentagon	Hexagon
Probability	0.38	0.26	0.15	0.21

Exam corner

1. A box contains pink, blue and yellow marker pens. The probability of selecting each colour pen from the box is:

Colour	Pink	Blue	Yellow
Probability	0.4	x	$2x$

   a) Work out the value of x

   [I got___/3 marks]

   b) Work out the probability of selecting a yellow pen. **[___/1 mark]**

2. The probability that Simon wins a game is $\frac{1}{5}$ and the probability of a draw is $\frac{1}{3}$

   a) Work out the probability that Simon loses the game. **[___/2 marks]**

   The probability that Simon wins a different game is $\frac{2}{x}$

   b) Work out an expression for the probability that Simon doesn't win this game. **[___/2 marks]**

See pages 128-129 for more practice

CLIMB TO 9

Outcomes and possibility spaces

A list or table showing all possible outcomes of an experiment or of combined experiments is called the **possibility space** or **sample space**.

To show a possibility space...
- make a systematic list of all possible outcomes
- for two combined experiments, make a two-way table showing the combinations or end results.

Formula box

Product rule for combined experiments

For *m* possible outcomes of one experiment and *n* possible outcomes of the other:

Number of possible combinations = $m \times n$

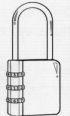

The padlock has digits 0–9 on each dial, so there are 10 possible outcomes for each of three dials.

Total number of combinations
= 10 × 10 × 10 = 1000

Worked example

Grade 4

As part of a board game, players must select a card from a pack and roll an ordinary dice.

Half of the cards have a number 2 on them and the rest have a number 3. The player must multiply the numbers on the card and the dice together.

a) Draw a table to show the possibility space.

[2 marks]

b) Work out the probability of scoring more than 10

[1 mark]

Solution

a) Multiply the two numbers together:

Dice

Card	1	2	3	4	5	6
2	2	4	6	8	10	12
3	3	6	9	12	15	18

b) There are 12 equally likely outcomes.

There are four outcomes which are more than 10

$P(\text{more than } 10) = \frac{4}{12} = \frac{1}{3}$

Worked example

Grade 6

A football team of 11 has four attacking players and seven defensive players (including the goalkeeper). Two players are to be selected to receive two different awards on behalf of the team. Two possible options for doing this are given. Work out the number of possible combinations for each.

Option 1: Select one attacking and one defensive player.

Option 2: Select any two different players.

[4 marks]

Solution

Option 1: 4 × 7 = 28 combinations

Option 2: 11 × 10 = 110 combinations

(since you can't pick the same player twice)

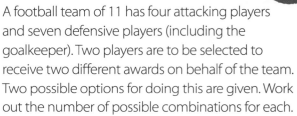

Exam corner

Grade 6

1. An access code for a website is of the form 'letter, letter, number'.
The possible letters are A, B, C, D, E.
The possible numbers are 1, 2, 3, 4, 5, 6, 7, 8
How many possible codes are there?
Circle the correct answer.

160   200   320   2197   **[I got __/1 mark]**

Grade 6

2. There are seven different types of drinks available at a café. Kyle goes to the café three times and buys a different drink each time. How many different ways can he do this?

[__/2 marks]

See pages 128–129 for more practice

CLIMB TO 9

Probability experiments

You can estimate the probability of an event from an experiment or from data.

Key points

- The estimated probability of an event is called the **relative frequency**.

  Relative frequency = $\dfrac{\text{number of times the event happened}}{\text{total number of trials}}$

- A **frequency tree** can be used to show outcomes of two or more events.

The more trials in the experiment, the more accurate the estimate of the probability.

Worked example

 Grade 4

The frequency tree shows the numbers of dogs and cats in a sample that have been microchipped.

a) A cat or dog is chosen at random. What is the probability it has been microchipped?
   [2 marks]

b) A dog is chosen at random. What is the probability it has not been microchipped?
   [2 marks]

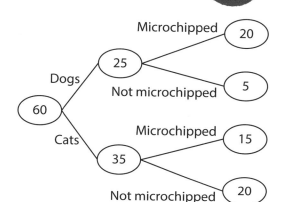

Notice how each column of numbers in this frequency tree adds up to the original total (60).

Solution

a) Total of microchipped cats and dogs = 20 + 15
                                        = 35

   Probability = $\dfrac{35}{60} = \dfrac{7}{12}$

b) You only need to consider the 25 dogs. 5 of them have not been microchipped, so

   Probability = $\dfrac{5}{25} = \dfrac{1}{5}$

Exam corner

 **Grade 4**   **Grade 6**

1. At a children's farmyard, one day there were 120 children and 80 adults. 30 children and 9 adults had a ride on the tractor and the rest had a ride in the trailer.

   a) Draw a frequency tree to show this information.
      [I got ___/3 marks]

   b) If a person is chosen at random, what is the probability that they rode on the trailer?   **[__/2 marks]**

2. Daisy has some milk, dark and white chocolates. She selects some of the chocolates at random and all but five are milk chocolate. She uses this result to estimate that the probability of milk chocolate is 0.8. Work out how many chocolates Daisy selected.
   [__/3 marks]

Examiner's tip!

When you draw a frequency tree, check that the numbers on the final branches add up to the total at the start.

Expected results

You can use probability to work out the number of times you expect a certain outcome.

Key points

- The **expected frequency** of an event is the number of times you expect it to happen.

  Expected frequency = probability × number of trials

- An unfair coin or spinner or dice is said to be **biased**.

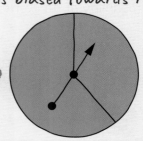

This spinner is unfair – it is biased towards red.

Confidence bar

Sorted!

Had a look

Worked example

 Grade 4

The probability that a person is left-handed is estimated to be 9%. There are 780 students in a school. Estimate how many are left-handed. **[2 marks]**

See page 7 for converting between percentages and decimals.

See page 2 for a reminder on rounding.

Solution

Expected frequency = 0.09 × 780
= 70.2

About 70 students are left-handed.

(Round the final answer as the number of students must be a whole number.)

Worked example   **Grade 4**

a) Miles rolls a dice 200 times and gets a 6 on 30 rolls. He claims this means the dice is biased. Do you think Miles is correct? Give a reason for your answer.   **[2 marks]**

b) Ben rolls a dice six times and doesn't get a 6. He claims this means the dice is biased to not land on 6. Do you think Ben is correct? Give a reason for your answer   **[1 mark]**

Solution

a) With a fair dice, the probability of a 6 is $\frac{1}{6}$
Expected frequency = $\frac{1}{6}$ × 200 = 33.333...
This is close to the actual result of 30, so Miles is wrong. The dice appears to be fair.

b) Ben is wrong, because six rolls are not enough trials to draw a conclusion.

Exam corner

1. In each case, give a reason whether or not the results suggest that the coin is biased.   **Grade 4**

   a) A coin is tossed six times and lands on heads only once.   **[I got __/1 mark]**

   b) A coin is tossed 100 times and lands on heads 25 times.   **[__/1 mark]**

2. In a computer game, when you open a box you receive a positive, a negative or a neutral result. The probability of each outcome is shown in the table.   **Grade 6**

Result	Positive	Negative	Neutral
Probability	$2x$		$3x$

If you open 20 boxes then you expect six positive results. How many negative results would you expect to get if you open 40 boxes? **[__/4 marks]**

The expected frequency won't always match the actual outcome as it's just the most likely of many possible outcomes. If it's really far off, though, the dice (or coin, spinner, etc.) is probably unfair.

Remember, the more trials in the experiment, the more accurate the estimate of the probability.

Tree diagrams

A **tree diagram** helps you to work out the probability of two or more events.

Grade 6–7

Key points

- You **multiply** probabilities along the branches to find the probability of two events occurring together.
- You **add** probabilities to find the probability of one <u>or</u> the other happening.

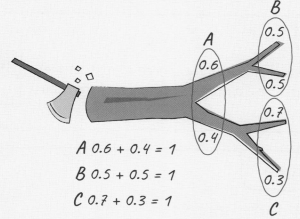

$A \ 0.6 + 0.4 = 1$

$B \ 0.5 + 0.5 = 1$

$C \ 0.7 + 0.3 = 1$

The probabilities on each set of branches add up to 1

Confidence bar

Sorted!

Had a look

Worked example

Grade 6

In a board game, you pick a dice randomly from a bag and roll it. The tree diagram shows the probabilities.

a) What is the value of x? **[1 mark]**

b) Work out the probability of picking a black dice and rolling a 6 **[2 marks]**

c) Work out the probability of rolling a 6 **[3 marks]**

Colour of dice   Number rolled

$\frac{1}{3}$ — Black $\frac{1}{4}$ — A six

$\frac{3}{4}$ — Not a six

$\frac{2}{3}$ — Red $\frac{1}{6}$ — A six

x — Not a six

Solution

a) Probabilities on each set of branches must add up to 1

$x = 1 - \frac{1}{6} = \frac{5}{6}$

b) $P(\text{black and six}) = \frac{1}{3} \times \frac{1}{4} = \frac{1}{12}$ Multiply along the branches.

c) There are two possible ways to roll a 6:

$P(\text{black and six}) = \frac{1}{12}$ (from part **b**)

$P(\text{red and six}) = \frac{2}{3} \times \frac{1}{6} = \frac{1}{9}$

These are mutually exclusive, so add them to find the probability of a 6:

$P(\text{six}) = \frac{1}{12} + \frac{1}{9} = \frac{7}{36}$

Exam corner

Grade 6

1. The probability that a year 11 student in a school studies Art is 0.2
If the student studies Art, the probability that they study Music is 0.1
If they do not study Art, the probability that they study Music is 0.4

a) Draw a tree diagram to represent this. **[I got ___/3 marks]**

b) Work out the probability that a year 11 student chosen at random

  i) doesn't study Art or Music   **ii)** studies Music. **[__/4 marks]**

2. A bag contains 3 red and 7 blue counters, and 2 counters are removed at random. By drawing a tree diagram, work out the probability that at least one of the removed counters is red. **[__/5 marks]**

Grade 7

The counters are not replaced, so the colour of the first counter affects the probabilities on the second set of branches e.g. if the first counter removed is red, then there are only 2 red counters left out of a total of 9

CLIMB TO 9 See pages 128-129 for more practice.

Conditional probability 1

Often one event happening affects the probability of another event. This is called **conditional probability**.

Key points

To work out a conditional probability, you need to restrict the sample space to the possible outcomes of the event that you know has occurred.

 See page 106 for more on sample spaces.

Worked example

 Grade 7

The two-way table records how a sample of 100 workers travel to work.

One of these workers is chosen at random.

Work out the probability that they

a) travel by car and are aged 31–50

[2 marks]

b) travel by car given they are aged 31–50

[2 marks]

Age (years)	Train/Bus	Walk	Car	Total
16–30	14	12	7	33
31–50	10	9	25	44
51–70	9	2	12	23
Total	33	23	44	100

Notice the difference between these two questions. A question about conditional probability often uses the word 'given'.

Solution

a) P(car <u>and</u> 31–50) $= \frac{25}{100} = \frac{1}{4}$

b) P(car <u>given</u> 31–50) $= \frac{25}{44}$ since you restrict the sample space to the 44 people who are aged 31–50

Exam corner

Grade 7

Amy works in a café. The two-way table shows some hot drink orders one morning.

A hot drink is randomly chosen from these orders.

a) Work out P(tea given milk).

Circle the correct answer.

$\frac{4}{5}$ $\frac{4}{15}$ $\frac{1}{3}$ $\frac{2}{5}$ **[I got __/1 mark]**

b) Amy claims that people are more likely to have milk in tea than in coffee.

Show that Amy is correct.   **[__/3 marks]**

	Tea	Coffee	Total
Milk	12	18	30
Cream	0	2	2
None	3	10	13
Total	15	30	45

 See page 111 for more on conditional probability.

Conditional probability 2

In some situations you need to use a formula to work out conditional probability.

Formula box

Use this formula to work out the probability of an outcome A, given that outcome B has occurred:

$$P(A \text{ given } B) = \frac{P(A \text{ and } B)}{P(B)}$$

Worked example

Grade 8

Syed plays two games, A and B. The tree diagram shows the probability of Syed winning or losing each game.

Using the tree diagram,

a) write P(wins B given wins A) **[1 mark]**
b) work out P(wins B) **[2 marks]**
c) work out P(wins A given wins B). **[2 marks]**

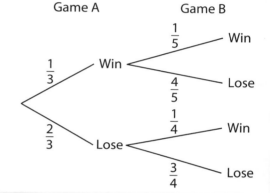

Solution

a) The probabilities on the second set of branches on a tree diagram are conditional on the events on the first set of branches. Therefore, you can just read from the diagram:

$$P(\text{wins B given wins A}) = \frac{1}{5}$$

b) Multiply along the branches:

$$P(\text{wins A and B}) = \frac{1}{3} \times \frac{1}{5} = \frac{1}{15}$$

$$P(\text{loses A and wins B}) = \frac{2}{3} \times \frac{1}{4} = \frac{1}{6}$$

$$P(\text{wins B}) = \frac{1}{15} + \frac{1}{6} = \frac{7}{30}$$

c) $P(\text{wins A given wins B}) = \dfrac{P(A \text{ and } B)}{P(B)} = \dfrac{\left(\frac{1}{15}\right)}{\left(\frac{7}{30}\right)} = \dfrac{2}{7}$

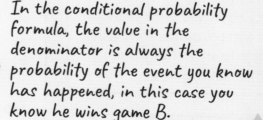

In the conditional probability formula, the value in the denominator is always the probability of the event you know has happened, in this case you know he wins game B.

Examiner's tip!

It's a good idea to draw a tree diagram for this type of question even if the question doesn't specifically tell you to.

Exam corner

Grade 9

A shop has jars of strawberry jam and raspberry jam in the ratio 3 : 1

Two customers come into the shop and randomly select a jar of jam to purchase.

The probability that both customers select strawberry jam is $\frac{11}{20}$

a) How many jars of jam does the shop have initially?

[I got ___/3 marks]

b) Given that the customers both chose the same type of jam, work out the probability that they both chose strawberry. **[___/3 marks]**

Set notation

A **set** is just a collection of numbers or objects. You need to know some special notation to describe sets and be able to draw **Venn diagrams** of sets.

Key points

- The symbol ξ means the **universal set**, which contains **all** the numbers.
- You can describe a set using curly brackets, e.g. {1, 2, 3, 4} or {odd numbers}.
- $x \in A$ means x is a member of the set A.
- $A \cap B$ means the **intersection** of sets A and B (numbers in **both** sets).
- $A \cup B$ means the **union** of sets A and B (numbers in **either** set).
- A' means the **complement** of set A (numbers **not** in set A).

$A \cap B$ $A \cup B$ A'

Examiner's tip!

The notation might seem tricky, but if you learn what each symbol means then you'll be able to answer any exam question on this topic.

Exam corner

1. For the Venn diagram in the worked example, write the numbers that are in set
   a) $A \cup B$ **[I got __/1 mark]**
   b) B' **[__/1 mark]**

2. ξ = {2, 4, 6, 8, 10, 12, 14, 16}

   Set X = {multiples of 4}
   Set Y = {10, 12, 14, 16}
   Draw a Venn diagram to show this information.
   [__/4 marks]

Worked example

ξ = {1, 2, 3, 4, 5, 6, 7, 8, 9, 10}

A = {odd numbers} B = {prime numbers}

a) Draw a Venn diagram to show this information. **[4 marks]**
b) Write the numbers that are in set $A \cap B$ **[1 mark]**

Solution

a)

The numbers in this section are in set A but not set B; they are odd but not prime.

The numbers in this section are in set A and set B; they are odd and prime.

2 is the only non-odd prime number.

The numbers in this section are not in set A nor in set B; they are non-prime and even.

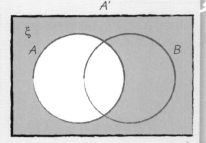

b) $A \cap B$ means the intersection of sets A and B.

The numbers in set $A \cap B$ are 3, 5 and 7

Probability from Venn diagrams

You can work out probabilities by drawing Venn diagrams.

To draw a Venn diagram with three sets...
- start in the middle with the numbers in all three sets
- then complete the numbers in two sets
- then the numbers in only one set and the numbers in none of the sets.

Worked example

Grade 8

There are 100 people at a swimming gala, 50 of whom are spectators. There are three races: freestyle, backstroke and breaststroke.

10 people compete in all three races.

25 people compete in backstroke and breaststroke.

20 people compete in backstroke and freestyle.

12 people compete in freestyle and breaststroke.

30 people compete in freestyle.

1 person competes in only backstroke.

a) Work out the probability that a randomly selected person will be competing in breaststroke. **[4 marks]**

b) A person is selected from the backstroke racers. What is the probability they are also competing in freestyle? **[2 marks]**

Notice that this question doesn't actually tell you to draw a Venn diagram. You need to decide on this strategy yourself.

Solution

a) First draw a Venn diagram:

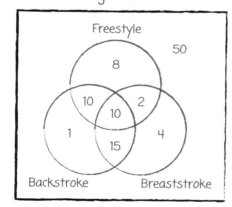

$$P(\text{breaststroke}) = \frac{10 + 15 + 2 + 4}{100} = \frac{31}{100}$$

b) Restrict the sample space to people competing in backstroke:
$$P(\text{freestyle given backstroke}) = \frac{10 + 10}{10 + 10 + 15 + 1}$$
$$= \frac{20}{36} = \frac{5}{9}$$

Exam corner

Grade 5

1. Some numbers are put into a Venn diagram.

A number is selected at random from the diagram.
Work out the probability the number is in set

a) A b) B c) $A \cap B$

d) $A \cup B$ e) A'

[I got __/5 marks]

2. The Venn diagram shows the sports clubs that a group of people attend.

Grade 7

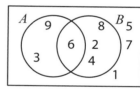

Work out the probability that a randomly chosen person from the group plays netball, given that they also play badminton. **[__/2 marks]**

See page 110 to remind yourself of conditional probability.

My notes

Climb to 9 – Introduction

We've carefully studied past exam papers and examiner reports to identify the trickiest question types. Work through the next 14 pages to give yourself the best possible chance of reaching Grade 9

Key points

- You'll find a 2-page spread to help you master each of the seven question types: p116-129
- These are not just the 'hardest' topics at the highest grade. For example, calculating with bounds is a topic generally assessed at Grade 6 or 7 difficulty, but still catches out students who are otherwise on track for a better grade.

- We've also indicated below where the basics for these topics are covered in the main content: p1-113
- For example, calculating with bounds is covered in this section on pages 116-117, but the basics are also covered in the main content on pages 4 & 61

The 'Climb to 9' approach

Grasping a maths topic is like climbing a mountain!

On each double-page spread, you'll find these three steps to help you master each topic:

① Getting the right equipment (Fluency)

Every expedition needs the right equipment: first check you have secure knowledge of the basic maths. You'll find a 'Check-up box' with a handful of 1 or 2-mark questions. Try these, look up the answers, and tick the green box if you've got them right. On each spread, a 'Need more help?' box will tell you where to look for more support.

② Starting the climb (Entry-level problems)

CLIMB TO 9

Building on the foundations, the next step is to try entry-level problems. Read through the 'Worked examples' here and then have a go at the problems in the 'Exam corner'. Take your time!

③ Reaching the summit (Problem solving)

All that preparation has been leading to this: problem-solving questions set in context. Again, carefully go through the 'Worked example' (typically a 4 or 5-marker), read the advice, and then go to the 'Exam corner'.

Climb to 9 topic	See page...	Need more help?
Calculating with bounds	116	4, 61
Forming & solving equations	118	16, 22-26, 32, 36
Forming algebraic proof	120	15, 23, 49, 55, 82
Tricky ratio questions	122	56, 57
Scale factor & similarity	124	64, 73
Applying sine and cosine rules	126	85, 89
Tricky probability questions	128	105, 106, 109

Examiner's tip!

When answering a <u>problem-solving question</u>, especially one with a lot of words, always start by <u>underlining the key information</u> and the <u>key instruction</u>. <u>Extract the information you need</u> **before** you start doing any maths.

Calculating with bounds

This section will look at calculations with values that have lower and upper bounds.

1 Getting the right equipment (*Fluency*)

Before you set out on an expedition, you need to get all the basics in place.

> OXFORD Revise

> "Grasping a maths topic is like climbing a mountain."

Check-up box

Grade
4–5

1. A car travels 18 miles in 30 minutes. Work out the average speed of the car in mph. ☐

2. I leave home at 08:00 and it takes 34 minutes to walk to the bus stop. I wait 14 minutes for my bus. The bus arrives at my destination at 09:22. How long was the bus journey? ☐

3. The answer to a calculation is 3.4 to 1 dp. Write the error interval for the number. ☐

4. Mila took 22 minutes, rounded to the nearest minute, to walk to school. Write the error interval for the time in minutes she took to get to school. ☐

> **Need more help?**
> Go to pages 4, 61

2 Starting the climb (*Entry-level problems*)

Once you have all the equipment, you are ready to start the climb.

Worked example

Grade
6

A room is 7.4 by 3.3 metres, measured to 1 decimal place.

By considering bounds, work out the maximum and minimum area of the room. **[4 marks]**

Solution

Lower and upper bound of length: $7.35 \leq l < 7.45$

Lower and upper bound of width: $3.25 \leq w < 3.35$

Lower bound of area: $7.35 \times 3.25 = 23.8875\,m^2$

Upper bound of area: $7.45 \times 3.35 = 24.9575\,m^2$

$23.8875\,m^2 \leq area < 24.9575\,m^2$

> Always work out the upper and lower bounds of the values <u>before</u> doing any calculation.

> Because you want the smallest possible solution from the multiplication, you need to use the two lower bound values.

> Take care to use the correct inequality signs.

Exam corner

Grade
6

Grade
6

1. Adam and Lee are brothers.

   Adam is 167 cm tall to the nearest cm.

   Lee is 146 cm tall to the nearest cm.

   Work out the maximum **difference** in their heights. **[I got __/3 marks]**

2. The radius of a circle is 5.6 cm to 2 significant figures.

   a) Give the minimum circumference of the circle. **[__/2 marks]**

   b) Give the maximum area of the circle. **[__/2 marks]**

③ Reaching the summit (*Problem solving*)

All that preparation and hard work has been building up to here: problem-solving questions set in context.

Worked example

Grade 7

 A race track measures <u>800 m</u> to the <u>nearest 10</u> metres.

A runner can run around the track in <u>178 s</u> to the <u>nearest second</u>.

Work out the runner's <u>speed</u> to a <u>suitable degree of accuracy</u>, and explain your answer.

[4 marks]

Solution

Upper bound of distance: 805 m

Lower bound of distance: 795 m

Upper bound of time: 178.5 s

Lower bound of time: 177.5 s

$\text{Speed} = \dfrac{\text{distance}}{\text{time}}$

Upper bound of speed: $\dfrac{805}{177.5} = 4.53... \text{ m/s}$

Lower bound of speed: $\dfrac{795}{178.5} = 4.45... \text{ m/s}$

You can say speed = 4.5 m/s to 2 sf, because the upper and the lower bound of the speed rounded to 2 significant figures are both 4.5 m/s.

> Start by underlining key information AND the instruction.

> Work out the upper and lower bounds of the values first.

> You want the largest possible solution from the division. So you need $\dfrac{\text{upper bound distance}}{\text{lower bound time}}$

> **Need more help?**
> Go to pages 4, 61

Exam corner

 3. The distance between two cities is 290 miles to the nearest 10 miles.

Grade 7

Fatima drives from one city to the other and believes her average speed will be 60 mph to the nearest 5 mph.

Estimate the time she will take to a suitable degree of accuracy. Give reasons for your answer. **[I got __/4 marks]**

 4. The triangle *ABC* has an area of 23 cm² to 2 significant figures.

Grade 9

$AB = 8.2$ cm to 2 significant figures and angle $A = 32°$ to 2 significant figures.

Work out the upper and lower bounds for *AC* to 3 significant figures. **[__/3 marks]**

> Use the formula:
> $\text{Area} = \dfrac{1}{2}ab\sin C$

Next steps...

List what you need to revise/practise:

.... ☐

.... ☐

.... ☐

.... ☐

.... ☐

.... ☐

Tick when done

Forming & solving equations

This section will look at problems in a context, and how to write equations to solve them.

Grade 4–9

① Getting the right equipment (*Fluency*)

Before you set out on an expedition, you need to get all the basics in place.

Check-up box

Need more help?
Go to pages 16, 22–26, 32

Grade 4–5

1. Make y the subject of $2y + 6x = 5$ ☐
2. Expand and simplify $(2x - 1)^2$ ☐
3. Factorise $x^2 + 5x - 14$ ☐
4. Solve $x^2 - 7x + 12 = 0$ ☐
5. Solve simultaneously $2x + y = 8$ and $x - y = 1$ ☐

"Grasping a maths topic is like climbing a mountain."

② Starting the climb (*Entry-level problems*)

Once you have all the equipment, you are ready to start the climb.

Worked example

Grade 5

<u>Hannah</u> is <u>older</u> than her sister Rosie.

The <u>sum</u> of their ages is <u>22</u> years.

The <u>difference</u> between their ages is <u>8 years</u>.

<u>Construct and solve two simultaneous equations</u> to work out the ages of Hannah and Rosie. **[4 marks]**

1) Start by underlining key information AND the instruction.

Solution

Hannah is x years old

Rosie is y years old.

$x + y = 22$ (1)

$x - y = 8$ (2)

2) Form equations using what you are told in the question. You know that Hannah is older.

(1) + (2): $2x = 30$ so $x = 15$

3) Solve using elimination.

$15 + y = 22$

4) Substitute the value of x into equation (1).

$y = 7$

$15 - 7 = 8$ ✓

5) Check this works in equation (2).

So Hannah is 15 years old and Rosie is 7

Exam corner

Grade 5

Grade 5

1. Sam is Max's younger brother. The difference between their ages is 5 years. In three years' time, Max will be three times Sam's age now. Work out the ages of Max and Sam. **[I got __/4 marks]**

2. Ezra has some 10p and 5p coins in his pocket. He has 12 coins altogether. The total of the coins is 80p. How many of each coin does Ezra have? **[__/4 marks]**

③ Reaching the summit (*Problem solving*)

All that preparation and hard work has been building up to these questions.

Worked example

Grade 8

Work out the value of the two distinct numbers x and y if:

x is <u>2 less</u> than y and

y is <u>equal to the square</u> of x **[5 marks]**

> Start by underlining key words.

Solution

$x = y - 2$
$y = x^2$

> Form the equations then follow the steps.

Step 1: $x = y - 2$

Step 2: $y = (y - 2)^2$
$\quad\quad y = y^2 - 4y + 4$

Step 3: $0 = y^2 - 5y + 4$
$\quad\quad 0 = (y - 4)(y - 1)$
$\quad\quad y = 4 \text{ or } y = 1$

Step 4: When $y = 4$, $x = 4 - 2$, $x = 2$
$\quad\quad$ When $y = 1$, $x = 1 - 2$, $x = -1$

> Remember, to solve simultaneous equations when one is linear and one is quadratic...
>
> STEP 1: Rearrange the linear equation to make x (or y) the subject.
> STEP 2: Substitute for x (or y) in the non-linear equation.
> STEP 3: Solve this quadratic equation to find two solutions for y (or x).
> STEP 4: Substitute each of these solutions back into the original linear equation to find corresponding solutions for x (or y).

Need more help?
Go to page 36

Exam corner

Grade 8

3. Solve the simultaneous equations
$\quad y = x^2 + x - 21$
$\quad y = 2x - 1$ **[I got __/4 marks]**

4. The difference between the two numbers a and b is 4, and the sum of the squares of these two numbers is 8. Form and solve two equations to find the values of a and b **[__/5 marks]**

Grade 8

5. The line $y = 2x + 1$ intersects the circle $x^2 + y^2 = 2$ at the points A and B. Work out the length of AB **[__/6 marks]**

Grade 9

Next steps...

List what you need to revise/practise:

- ☐
- ☐
- ☐
- ☐
- ☐

Tick when done

Forming algebraic proof

This section will provide further practice with algebraic proof, including questions where you need to use diagrams.

1 Getting the right equipment (*Fluency*)

Before you set out on an expedition, you need to get all the basics in place.

Check-up box

Grade 4

1. Write down the nth term of the sequence $-12, -14, -16, -18, \ldots$
2. Write down the nth term of the sequence $11, 13, 15, 17, \ldots$
3. Simplify $5x + 7 - 2(x - 5)$
4. Simplify $n^2 + 4 - (n + 2)^2$

📋 **Need more help?**
Go to pages 15, 49

"Grasping a maths topic is like climbing a mountain."

2 Starting the climb (*Entry-level problems*)

Once you have all the equipment, you are ready to start the climb.

Worked example

Grade 6

The area of the trapezium shown is $56\,\text{cm}^2$.

a) Show that $3x^2 - 4x - 55 = 0$ **[3 marks]**
b) Work out the perpendicular height of the trapezium. **[3 marks]**

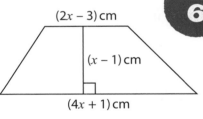

$(2x - 3)\,\text{cm}$
$(x - 1)\,\text{cm}$
$(4x + 1)\,\text{cm}$

Solution

a)   Area of a trapezium $= \frac{1}{2}(a + b)h$ *Write down the formula you need to use.*

$\frac{1}{2}((4x + 1) + (2x - 3))(x - 1) = 56$ *Substitute in the expressions for a, b and h.*

$\frac{1}{2}(6x - 2)(x - 1) = 56$

$(3x - 1)(x - 1) = 56$

$3x^2 - 4x + 1 = 56$

$3x^2 - 4x - 55 = 0$

b) $(3x + 11)(x - 5) = 0$
$3x + 11 = 0$ or $x - 5 = 0$
$x = \left(-\frac{11}{3}\right), 5$ *Ignore the negative value for x because you can't have negative length.*
Height of trapezium $= 5 - 1 = 4\,\text{cm}$

Exam corner

Grade 6

1. A right-angled triangle has sides $(x + 2)\,\text{cm}$, $(x + 1)\,\text{cm}$ and $x\,\text{cm}$.
   a) Using the diagram, show that $x^2 - 2x - 3 \equiv 0$ **[I got __/3 marks]**
   b) Work out the length of each side of the triangle. **[__/3 marks]**

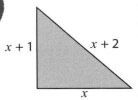

$x + 1$ $x + 2$

x

📋 **Need more help?**
Go to pages 23, 8

3 Reaching the summit (*Problem solving*)

All that preparation and hard work has been building up to here: problem-solving questions set in context.

It is a really good idea to be confident in writing the following in algebraic terms:

Any two numbers: n, m

An even number: $2n$

An odd number: $2n + 1$

Consecutive numbers: $n, n + 1, n + 2, ...$

Consecutive even numbers: $2n, 2n + 2, ...$
Any two even numbers: $2n, 2m$

Consecutive odd numbers: $2n - 1, 2n + 1, 2n + 3, ...$
Any two odd numbers: $2n + 1, 2m + 1$

Worked example

Grade 8

Prove that the <u>sum</u> of <u>two consecutive square numbers</u> is an <u>odd</u> number. **[3 marks]**

> Underline key words.

Solution

A number = n

The next number = $n + 1$

This squared = n^2

This squared = $(n + 1)^2$

> Break it down into the individual parts. You underlined 'two consecutive square numbers', so start with two consecutive numbers and square them.

The sum of the squares is $n^2 + (n + 1)^2$

Expand:

$n^2 + (n + 1)^2 \equiv n^2 + n^2 + 2n + 1$

$= 2n^2 + 2n + 1$

$= 2(n^2 + n) + 1$

> **Need more help?**
> Go to page 55

> You have now assembled the information you need to complete the proof.

Since $2(n^2 + n)$ is a multiple of 2, it is even, and adding 1 to an even number will give an odd number.

> Don't forget a final sentence to answer the question.

Exam corner

Grade 7

2. Show that $(4n + 1)^2 - (4n - 1)^2$ is always a multiple of 16 for positive integer values of n

[I got __/3 marks]

3. Prove that the difference between the squares of two consecutive integers is always equal to the sum of the two integers. **[__/4 marks]**

Grade 8

4. Here are the first few terms of an arithmetic sequence: 2, 6, 10, 14, 18
Prove that the difference between the squares of any two terms of the sequence is a multiple of 32
[__/4 marks]

Grade 9

Next steps...

List what you need to revise/practise:

- .... ☐
- .... ☐
- .... ☐
- .... ☐
- .... ☐

Tick when done

Tricky ratio questions

This section will look at how to tackle longer ratio questions in a context.

1 Getting the right equipment (*Fluency*)

Before you set out on an expedition, you need to get all the basics in place.

Check-up box

📄 **Need more help?**
Go to page 56

Grade 4

1. The ratio of red to yellow counters in a game is 2:5. There are 36 more yellow counters than red ones. How many red counters are there? ☐

2. Three-quarters of the apples in a box are red, the rest are green. Write down the ratio of red to green. ☐

3. Ruby, Nur and Lola share some money in the ratio 3:4:5. Lola gets £30. How much does Ruby get? ☐

"Grasping a maths topic is like climbing a mountain."

2 Starting the climb (*Entry-level problems*)

Once you have all the equipment, you are ready to start the climb.

Worked example

Grade 5

In a group of boys and girls, the ratio of boys to girls is 2:3. 25% of the boys are left-handed. $\frac{1}{3}$ of the girls are left-handed.

What percentage of the overall group is right-handed?

[4 marks]

1) Start by underlining key information.

Solution

Boys | L | | | |
Girls | | L | | |

2) Split the boys' 2 boxes into 4 to show 25% are left-handed, and mark $\frac{1}{3}$ of the girls' boxes as left-handed.

Boys | L | | | |
Girls | L | L | | | |

3) You need to make all the boxes the same size. Count the boxes representing right-handed students.

The fraction of the group that is right-handed is $\frac{7}{10}$, so the percentage is 70%.

Exam corner

Grade 5

1. Daniel inherits some money from a relative. He spends 25% of the money on a new bike.

   He puts $\frac{2}{3}$ of the remaining amount in a savings account.

   He splits the money that hasn't been spent or put into a savings account in the ratio 1:3 between his two cousins James and Florence.

   If Florence gets £300, how much did Daniel inherit? **[I got __/4 marks]**

③ Reaching the summit (*Problem solving*)

All that preparation and hard work has been building up to here: problem-solving questions set in context.

Worked example

The points P, Q, R and S lie in order on a straight line such that

$PQ:QS = 3:4$ and

$PR:RS = 9:5$

Work out $PQ:QR:RS$ **[4 marks]**

Solution

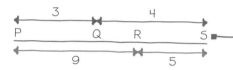

> First draw a diagram to show the different ratios on the line.

$PQ:QS = 3:4$ total 7 parts
$PR:RS = 9:5$ total 14 parts

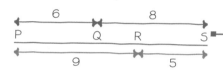

> Change 3:4 to 6:8 so that each ratio has the same total number of parts.

P to Q = 6 parts, P to R = 9 parts, so Q to R = 3 parts

> You can see that P to Q is 6 and P to R is 9, so use this to work out Q to R

Check using the other values:

Q to S = 8 parts, R to S = 5 parts, so Q to R = 3 parts ✓

$PQ:QR:RS = 6:3:5$

📄 **Need more help?**
Go to page 57

Examiner's tip!

Always look for ways to go back and check your working out is correct.

Exam corner

2. On a farm, the ratio of chickens to sheep is $7:2$ and the ratio of sheep to pigs is $3:1$. The total number of chickens, sheep and pigs is 116

Work out the number of pigs on the farm.

[I got ___/4 marks]

3. A roller hockey club has sticks and balls in the ratio $3:2$. If two sticks break and three balls are lost, then the ratio of sticks to balls is $8:5$
Work out the number of sticks and balls that were there at the start.

[___/4 marks]

Next steps...

List what you need to revise/practise:

.... ☐

.... ☐

.... ☐

.... ☐

.... ☐

Tick when done

Scale factor & similarity

This section will look at applying scale factors for length, area and volume to questions involving similar shapes.

Grade 5–8

1 Getting the right equipment (*Fluency*)

Before you set out on an expedition, you need to get all the basics in place.

Check-up box

Need more help?
Go to page 64

Grade 5

1. Convert $3\,cm^2$ to mm^2.
2. Convert $3000\,cm^3$ to m^3.
3. A square has area $25\,cm^2$. Work out the side length in mm.
4. A cuboid has volume $0.004\,m^3$. Give the volume in mm^3.

"Grasping a maths topic is like climbing a mountain."

2 Starting the climb (*Entry-level problems*)

Once you have all the equipment, you are ready to start the climb.

Worked example

Grade 7

Two <u>similar</u> cylinders have radius r and $2r$
The <u>volume</u> of the <u>large</u> cylinder is <u>1.84 m³</u>.
<u>Work out</u> the <u>volume</u> of the <u>small</u> cylinder
in <u>cm³</u>. **[4 marks]**

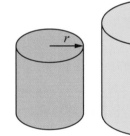

Solution

The length of the radius has been increased by a scale factor of 2
The volume will be increased by a scale factor of 2^3

> Start by underlining key information and instructions.

The volume of the large cylinder is $1.84\,m^3$, so the volume of the small cylinder will be $1.84 \div 2^3 = 0.23\,m^3$
In cm^3, this is $0.23 \times 100^3 = 230\,000\,cm^3$

> Careful: the units are not in the form asked for in the question.

Exam corner

Grade 5

Grade 7

1. A cube has volume $216\,000\,cm^3$. The outside of the cube is to be painted. Paint is sold in tins that cover $2\,m^2$. Work out how many tins are needed. **[I got __/4 marks]**

2. A and B are similar 3D shapes. A has surface area $30\,m^2$ and B has surface area $270\,m^2$. Write the ratio of the length of A to the length of B **[__/3 marks]**

3 Reaching the summit (*Problem solving*)

All that preparation and hard work has been building up to here: problem-solving questions set in context.

Worked example

Grade 8

Three 3D shapes, *A*, *B* and *C*, are mathematically similar.

The ratio of the surface area of shape *A* to that of *B* is 16:9 ◄── Start by underlining key information and instructions.

The volume of *B* is 216 cm³.

The volume of *C* is 125 cm³.

Work out the ratio of the heights in the form *A* : *B* : *C*　　**[4 marks]**

Solution

The easiest way to compare all the ratios is in a table.

	A	:	*B*	:	*C*
Surface area	16	:	9		
Height	$\sqrt{16}$	:	$\sqrt{9}$		
Height	4	:	3		
Volume			216	:	125
Height			$\sqrt[3]{216}$	:	$\sqrt[3]{125}$
Height			6	:	5
Height	4	:	③/⑥	:	5
Ratio	8	:	6	:	5

You take the square root of the area ratio to find the ratio of heights.

To compare the ratios you need to make the *B* values the same. So double the ratio of *A* : *B*.

📄 **Need more help?**
Go to page 73

Exam corner

Grade 8

3. The radius of the base of a cone is 12 cm. A similar, smaller cone is removed to leave a frustum. The volume of the frustum is $\frac{7}{8}$ of the volume of the larger cone.

Work out the radius of the smaller cone.

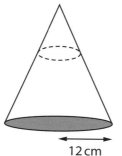

12 cm　　**[I got __/3 marks]**

Next steps...

List what you need to revise/practise:

.... ☐

.... ☐

.... ☐

.... ☐

.... ☐

Tick when done

Applying sine & cosine rules

Grade 4–9

This section will look at how to use the sine and cosine rules in questions about bearings.

① Getting the right equipment (*Fluency*)

Before you set out on an expedition, you need to get all the basics in place.

Need more help? Go to page 85

Check-up box

Grade 4

1. Gaby walks due west from home. Write her bearing from home. ☐
2. The bearing of *B* from *A* is 073°. Work out the bearing of *A* from *B* ☐
3. Thomas cycles 8 km south-east from *P* to *R*. Work out the bearing of *P* from *R* ☐

"Grasping a maths topic is like climbing a mountain."

② Starting the climb (*Entry-level problems*)

Once you have all the equipment, you are ready to start the climb.

Worked example

Grade 8

A boat sails south 10 km from *A* to *B*. Then it sails from *B* to *C* on a bearing of 125° for 6 km, and then directly back to *A*
Work out the total distance travelled, to 2 dp.

[4 marks]

First draw a sketch to show the information. Label the sides and angles.

Solution

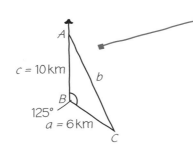

Use the cosine rule to find side *b*

$b^2 = a^2 + c^2 - 2ac\cos B$
$b^2 = 6^2 + 10^2 - (2 \times 6 \times 10 \times \cos 125°)$
$b^2 = 136 - (-68.82917...)$
$b^2 = 204.82917...$
$b = 14.31$ to 2 dp

Total distance = 14.31 + 6 + 10 = 30.31 km

Use the flow chart on page 89 to decide whether to use the sine or the cosine rule.

Exam corner

Grade 8

1. A triangular garden has the measurements shown on the diagram.
   Work out the length of fence, to 2 dp, needed to go all the way around the garden. **[I got ___/5 marks]**

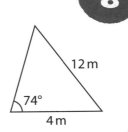

Need more help? Go to page 89

③ Reaching the summit (*Problem solving*)

All that preparation and hard work has been building up to here: problem-solving questions set in context.

Worked example

Three farmhouses, *A*, *B*, and *C*, are located as shown on the diagram.

B is 13 km from *A* on a bearing of 060°.

C is 10 km from *A*

Angle *ACB* is 42°.

a) Work out the <u>bearing of *C* from *A*</u>   **[5 marks]**
The farms are to be shown on a map with <u>scale 1 : 200 000</u>

b) What length in cm will show the <u>distance from *A* to *C*?</u>   **[1 mark]**

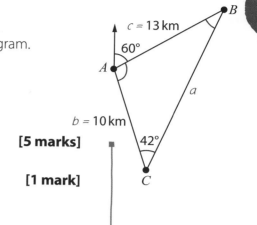

Grade 9

Solution

> First underline key information and instructions. Refer to the diagram.

> Work out which angle you are trying to find. Label the sides and angles and decide what information you need.

a) $\dfrac{\sin B}{10} = \dfrac{\sin 42°}{13}$

$B = 30.978...°$

$A = 180 - 42 - 30.978... = 107°$

The bearing of *C* from *A* is 60 + 107 = 167°

> You don't have enough information to work out side *a* or angle *A*, so you need to work out the angle *B* first. Use the sine rule.

b) $b = 10$ km $= 10 × 1000 × 100 = 1000000$ cm
On the map this will be 1000000 ÷ 200000 = 5 cm

> **Need more help?**
> Go to pages 85, 89

Exam corner

Grade 9

2. Ahmad walks 20 m from *X* to *Y* on a bearing of 130°. He then walks 52 m on a bearing of 242° from *Y* to *Z*. Finally he walks directly back to *X*

a) How far has Ahmad walked in total, in m to 2 dp?
[I got __/5 marks]

b) Ahmad wants to draw a map of his walk using a scale of 1 : 1000. What length in cm will show the distance from *X* to *Y*?   **[__/1 mark]**

Examiner's tip!

Start by drawing a diagram.

Next steps...

List what you need to revise/practise:

☐ ☐ ☐ ☐ ☐

Tick when done

Tricky probability questions

This section will look at how to apply basic maths skills to those tricky probability questions that often catch students out.

① Getting the right equipment (*Fluency*)

Before you set out on an expedition, you need to get all the basics in place.

"Grasping a maths topic is like climbing a mountain."

Check-up box

Need more help?
Go to pages 105, 106

Grade 4–5

1. The probability that a student is on time for school is 0.6, and the probability that a student has a hot school meal is $\frac{2}{3}$. Work out the probability that a student has a hot school meal and is on time for school. ☐

2. The probability that it will rain tomorrow is $\frac{3}{x}$. Work out the probability that it won't rain. ☐

② Starting the climb (*Entry-level problems*)

Once you have all the equipment, you are ready to start the climb.

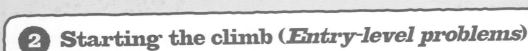

Worked example

Grade 7

There are purple and blue balls in a bag. Picking a blue ball is twice as likely as picking a purple ball.

a) Explain why the probability of picking a blue ball is $\frac{2}{3}$ **[2 marks]**

b) One ball is chosen at random. The ball is then replaced and a second ball is taken. Draw a tree diagram to show the probabilities of the results. **[3 marks]**

c) Charlie says you are most likely to get two balls of the same colour. Is he correct? Give a reason for your answer. **[2 marks]**

Solution

a) (Picking blue):(picking purple) = 2:1. So out of 3 picks, 2 will be blue. Therefore, P(blue) = $\frac{2}{3}$

b)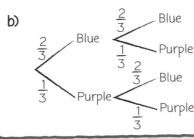

c) P(two blue) = $\frac{2}{3} \times \frac{2}{3} = \frac{4}{9}$ P(two purple) = $\frac{1}{3} \times \frac{1}{3} = \frac{1}{9}$

P(two same colour) = $\frac{4}{9} + \frac{1}{9} = \frac{5}{9}$

So P(not same colour) = $1 - \frac{5}{9} = \frac{4}{9}$

Charlie is correct because $\frac{5}{9}$ is bigger than $\frac{4}{9}$

Need more help?
Go to page 109

Exam corner

Grade 8

1. The ratio of red:white:black socks is 2:3:1. Initially there are 9 white socks.

Two socks are picked at random without replacement.

a) Draw a tree diagram to represent the probabilities of the results. **[I got ___/3 marks]**

b) Work out the probability of picking two socks of the same colour. **[___/2 marks]**

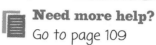
3 Reaching the summit (*Problem solving*)

All that preparation and hard work has been building up to here: problem-solving questions set in context.

Worked example

In a bag there are x balls. They are either pink or green. There are three green balls.

Two balls are picked at random <u>without replacement</u>.

a) Show the probability of the first ball picked being pink is $\dfrac{x-3}{x}$ **[1 mark]**

b) Draw a tree diagram to show the probabilities. **[3 marks]**

c) Write an expression for the probability of getting two pink balls. **[3 marks]**

> Underline key information.

> 📄 **Need more help?**
> Go to page 109

Solution

a) The total number of balls in the bag is x. There are 3 green balls so there are $x - 3$ pink balls.

So, P(pink) = $\dfrac{x-3}{x}$

b)

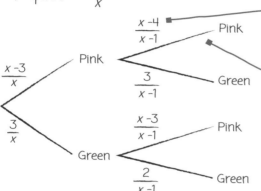

> You need to subtract 1 from the numerator because the pink ball taken is not replaced, so there is 1 less pink ball in the bag.

> You need to subtract 1 from the denominator because the ball picked first is not replaced, so there is 1 less ball to choose from.

c) P(two pink) = $\dfrac{x-3}{x} \times \dfrac{x-4}{x-1} = \dfrac{(x-3)(x-4)}{x(x-1)}$

Exam corner

2. A certain disease occurs in the population with probability x. A screening procedure is available and in 8 out of 10 cases where the patient has the disease, it produces a positive result. If the patient does not have the disease, there is a $0.5x$ chance that the test will give an incorrect positive result. Dina is tested for the disease.

a) Draw a tree diagram to show the above information. Let D represent the event 'Dina has the disease' and S represent the event 'Screening gives a positive result'. **[I got ___/4 marks]**

b) Work out the probability that Dina does not have the disease but gets a positive result in the screening test. **[___/1 mark]**

c) The probability of a negative result given you have the disease is 0.002. Use this to work out the probability that a randomly picked person in the population has the disease. **[___/2 marks]**

Next steps...

List what you need to revise/practise:

☐
☐
☐
☐
☐

Tick when done

When drawing the tree diagram, the first set of branches should relate solely to whether someone has the disease or not; the second set to the screening.

Guided answers

Page 1, Calculations

1. $15 - 12\sqrt{(34 + 9(-2))} = 15 - 12\sqrt{(34 - 18)}$
$$= 15 - 12\sqrt{16}$$
$$= 15 - 12 \times 4$$
$$= 15 - 48$$
$$= -33$$

1 mark *for correct answer circled.*

2. Deal 1:
$97 + 26.82 \times 24 = 97 + 643.68 = £740.68$
Deal 2:
$20.35 \times 36 = £732.60$
Deal 2 is the best value.
1 mark *for correctly calculating 26.82×24;* *1 mark* *for correct total for Deal 1;* *1 mark* *for correct total for Deal 2;* *1 mark* *for correct conclusion (must have all the supporting working). Total 4 marks.*

Page 2, Rounding & truncation

1. a i 62 000   **ii** 62 400   **iii** 62 357.9
1 mark *for each correct answer. Total 3 marks.*
b 62 357
1 mark *for correct answer.*

2. $2.25 \div 8 = 0.281\,25$
       $= 0.28$ kg to 2 significant figures
Alternatively:
$2250 \div 8 = 281.25$
       $= 280$ g to 2 significant figures
1 mark *for correctly dividing by 8;* *1 mark* *for rounding your answer to 2 sf.*

Page 3, Estimation

1. Time $= \frac{5.891 \times 52}{204.2} \approx \frac{6 \times 50}{200} = 1.5$ hours
1 mark *for using time $= \frac{distance}{speed}$;* *1 mark* *for rounding all values to 1 sf;* *1 mark* *for correct answer. Total 3 marks.*

2. 125 is between 121 and 144 but closer to 121
$\sqrt{125} \approx 11.2$
1 mark *for value between 11 and 12;* *1 mark* *for either 11.1 or 11.2 given.*

Page 4, Error intervals & bounds

1. a $229.5 \le c < 230.5$
1 mark *for both values correct, even if you use < instead of ≤ (or vice-versa);* *1 mark* *for fully correct answer with correct inequality signs.*
b $230 \le c < 240$
1 mark *for both values correct, even if you use < instead of ≤ (or vice-versa);* *1 mark* *for fully correct answer with correct inequality signs.*

2. Lower bound for area $= 18.45 \times 9.285$
                $= 171.308\,25$ cm^2
Upper bound for area $= 18.55 \times 9.295$
                $= 172.422\,25$ cm^2

Both upper and lower bounds round to 170 to 2 significant figures.
Area $= 170$ cm^2
1 mark *for finding the upper and lower bounds of the length;* *1 mark* *for finding the upper and lower bounds of the width;* *1 mark* *for finding lower bound for area;* *1 mark* *for finding upper bound for area;* *1 mark* *for correct solution with reason. Total 5 marks.*

Page 5, Adding & subtracting fractions

1. $1\frac{8}{9} + \frac{5}{6} = \frac{17}{9} + \frac{5}{6} = \frac{34}{18} + \frac{15}{18} = \frac{49}{18}$
$\frac{49}{18} - \frac{1}{18} = \frac{48}{18} = 2\frac{12}{18} = 2\frac{2}{3}$
The tub weighs $2\frac{2}{3}$ kg.

1 mark *for writing $\frac{5}{6}$ and $\frac{8}{9}$ (or $\frac{17}{9}$) over a common denominator (e.g. 18, 36 or 54);* *1 mark* *for finding $\frac{49}{18}$ (or equivalent);* *1 mark* *for subtracting $\frac{1}{18}$ from your sum found (or from $\frac{5}{6}$ or $1\frac{8}{9}$);* *1 mark* *for correct answer as mixed number and in simplest form. Total 4 marks.*

2. a $\frac{9}{50} - \frac{11}{75} = \frac{27}{150} - \frac{22}{150} = \frac{5}{150} = \frac{1}{30}$
1 mark *for writing both fractions over a common denominator;* *1 mark* *for correct answer in any form;* *1 mark* *for correct, fully simplified answer. Total 3 marks.*
b $1\frac{1}{12} + \frac{8}{9} = \frac{13}{12} + \frac{8}{9} = \frac{39}{36} + \frac{32}{36} = \frac{71}{36}$ or $1\frac{35}{36}$
1 mark *for writing $1\frac{1}{12}$ as an improper fraction;* *1 mark* *for writing both fractions over a common denominator;* *1 mark* *for correct, fully simplified answer. Total 3 marks.*
Alternatively:
$1\frac{1}{12} + \frac{8}{9} = 1 + \frac{3}{36} + \frac{32}{36} = 1\frac{35}{36}$ or $\frac{71}{36}$
1 mark *for writing $1\frac{1}{12}$ as $1 + \frac{1}{12}$;* *1 mark* *for writing both $\frac{1}{12}$ and $\frac{8}{9}$ over a common denominator;* *1 mark* *for correct, fully simplified answer as a mixed number or an improper fraction. Total 3 marks.*

Page 6, Multiplying & dividing fractions

1. $\frac{3}{4} \div \frac{5}{14} = \frac{3}{4} \times \frac{14}{5} = \frac{42}{20} = 2\frac{2}{20} = 2\frac{1}{10}$
1 mark *for correct answer circled.*

2. Total amount of drink $= \frac{3}{8} \times \frac{9}{2} = \frac{27}{16}$ litre
Number of cups $= \frac{27}{16} \div \frac{3}{16} = \frac{27}{16} \times \frac{16}{3} = \frac{27}{3} = 9$
1 mark *for finding total amount of the drink;* *1 mark* *for dividing by $\frac{3}{16}$;* *1 mark* *for correct answer. Total 3 marks.*

Page 7, Fractions, decimals & percentages

1. $\frac{3}{8} = 3 \div 8 = 0.375 = 37.5\%$

37.5% + 13% = 50.5%

100% − 50.5% = 49.5%

49.5% are travelling for leisure.

1 mark for converting $\frac{3}{8}$ to a percentage; 1 mark for subtracting two percentages from 100%; 1 mark for correct answer. Total 3 marks.

2. $\frac{21}{98} = \frac{3}{14}$

$14 = 2 \times 7$

Therefore, the fraction is a recurring decimal since the denominator has prime factors other than 2 and 5

1 mark for simplifying and considering prime factors of denominator; 1 mark for conclusion.

Page 8, Recurring decimals

1. **a** $\quad 0.1\ 4\ 2\ 8\ 5\ 7\ 1\quad$ etc.

$7\overline{)1\ .\ ^10\ ^30\ ^20\ ^60\ ^40\ ^50\ ^10}$

$\frac{1}{7} = 0.\dot{1}4285\dot{7}$

1 mark for attempting long or short division; 1 mark for completely correct answer with dots in correct places.

b Let $x = 0.777\ldots$

$10x = 7.777\ldots$

$10x - x = 7.777\ldots - 0.777\ldots$

$9x = 7$

$x = \frac{7}{9}$

1 mark for finding 10x and subtracting x; 1 mark for correct answer with all working correct.

2. Let $x = 0.3242424\ldots$

$10x = 3.242424\ldots$

$1000x = 324.2424\ldots$

$1000x - 10x = 324.2424\ldots - 3.242424\ldots$

$990x = 321$

$x = \frac{321}{990}$

$x = \frac{107}{330}$

1 mark for finding 1000x and 10x and subtracting; 1 mark for correct answer in any form; 1 mark for fully simplified answer. Total 3 marks.

Page 9, Surds

1. **a** $\sqrt{24} = \sqrt{4}\sqrt{6} = 2\sqrt{6}$

1 mark for correct answer.

b $\sqrt{98} - \sqrt{50} = \sqrt{49}\sqrt{2} - \sqrt{25}\sqrt{2}$

$\qquad\qquad\qquad = 7\sqrt{2} - 5\sqrt{2} = 2\sqrt{2}$

1 mark for simplifying $\sqrt{98}$ and $\sqrt{50}$; 1 mark for correct answer.

c $\frac{6}{\sqrt{3}} = \frac{6\sqrt{3}}{\sqrt{3}\sqrt{3}} = \frac{6\sqrt{3}}{3} = 2\sqrt{3}$

1 mark for multiplying numerator and denominator by $\sqrt{3}$; 1 mark for correct answer.

2. $\frac{3+\sqrt{7}}{3-\sqrt{7}} = \frac{(3+\sqrt{7})^2}{(3-\sqrt{7})(3+\sqrt{7})}$

$\qquad\qquad = \frac{9 + 6\sqrt{7} + 7}{9 - 7}$

$\qquad\qquad = \frac{16 + 6\sqrt{7}}{2} = 8 + 3\sqrt{7}$

1 mark for attempting to multiply numerator and denominator by $(3 + \sqrt{7})$; 1 mark for correct expansion of both numerator and denominator (do not need to be simplified); 1 mark for final answer in correct form. Total 3 marks.

Page 10, Index notation

1. $\left(\frac{3}{5}\right)^{-2} = \left(\frac{9}{25}\right)^{-1} = \frac{25}{9}$

1 mark for correct answer circled.

2. $\sqrt{8} = (2^3)^{\frac{1}{2}} = 2^{\frac{3}{2}}$

$n = \frac{3}{2}$

1 mark for writing 8 as 2^3 and using $\frac{1}{2}$ for square root; 1 mark for multiplying powers; 1 mark for correct value of n. Total 3 marks.

Page 11, Prime factor decomposition

1. **a** $54 = 2 \times 3 \times 3 \times 3 = 2 \times 3^3$

2 marks for correct answer in correct form, or 1 mark for answer not in index form.

b $650 = 2 \times 5 \times 5 \times 13 = 2 \times 5^2 \times 13$

2 marks for correct answer in correct form, or 1 mark for answer not in index form.

2. $6 = 2 \times 3$, $14 = 2 \times 7$ and $50 = 2 \times 5^2$

Therefore, number is $2 \times 3 \times 7 \times 5^2$

(or $2 \times 3 \times 7 \times 5 \times 5$)

1 mark for using $6 = 2 \times 3$ or $14 = 2 \times 7$ or $50 = 2 \times 5^2$; 1 mark for correct answer.

Page 12, Working out HCF and LCM

1. **a**

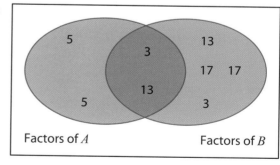

Factors of A Factors of B

HCF $= 3 \times 13$

1 mark for drawing a correct Venn diagram, or for other valid method such as writing out the factors and circling; 1 mark for recognising answer as 3×13; 1 mark for answer in index form. Total 3 marks.

b LCM $= 3 \times 3 \times 5 \times 5 \times 13 \times 13 \times 17 \times 17$

$\qquad\quad = 3^2 \times 5^2 \times 13^2 \times 17^2$

1 mark for writing out product of factors; 1 mark for answer in index form.

2. HCF $= 14 \Rightarrow y = 2$

N is $2 \times 7 \times 2 = 28$

LCM $= 420 \Rightarrow 420 = 2 \times P$

P is $420 \div 2 = 210$

1 mark for finding correct value of y; 1 mark for finding $N = 28$; 1 mark for method to find P (either divide LCM by 2 or find $x = 5$ then multiply factors together); 1 mark for finding 210. Total 4 marks.

Page 13, Standard form

1. 0.000 002 01 m

1 mark for correct answer circled.

2. Saturn to Jupiter $= 6.46 \times 10^7$ km

Jupiter is closer to Saturn than Uranus is since smaller power of 10

Alternatively:

Saturn to Uranus $= 1450\,000\,000$ km

Jupiter is closer to Saturn than Uranus is since

$64\,600\,000 < 1450\,000\,000$

1 mark for converting one distance into standard form / ordinary number; 1 mark for correct conclusion (must have converted).

Page 14, Calculating with standard form

1. a $\begin{array}{r} \overset{3\,1\,1}{42\,000\,000} \\ -\ 6\,100\,000 \\ \hline 35\,900\,000 \end{array}$ which is 3.59×10^7

1 mark for converting both to ordinary numbers (or writing both with the same power of 10); 1 mark for correct subtraction; 1 mark for correct answer in standard form. Total 3 marks.

b $(9 \times 10^{-7}) \times (8 \times 10^5) = (9 \times 8) \times (10^{-7} \times 10^5)$

$= 72 \times 10^{-2}$

$= 7.2 \times 10^{-1}$

1 mark for attempting to multiply 9 by 8 and add the powers; 1 mark for correct answer in any form; 1 mark for correct answer in standard form. Total 3 marks.

c $(2.4 \times 10^{-7}) \div (9.6 \times 10^{-5}) = (2.4 \div 9.6) \times (10^{-7} \div 10^{-5})$

$= 0.25 \times 10^{-2}$

$= 2.5 \times 10^{-3}$

1 mark for attempting to divide 2.4 by 9.6 and subtracting the powers of 10; 1 mark for correct answer in any form; 1 mark for correct answer in standard form. Total 3 marks.

d $(7.7 \times 10^5) \div (1.1 \times 10^{-3}) \times (3 \times 10^4)$

$= (7.7 \div 1.1 \times 3) \times (10^5 \div 10^{-3} \times 10^4)$

$= 21 \times 10^{12}$

$= 2.1 \times 10^{13}$

1 mark for attempting to calculate $7.7 \div 1.1 \times 3$ and subtracting/adding the powers of 10; 1 mark for correct answer in any form; 1 mark for correct answer in standard form. Total 3 marks.

2. $(2.1 \times 10^4) \div (3 \times 10^6) = (2.1 \div 3) \times (10^4 \div 10^6)$

$= 0.7 \times 10^{-2}$

$= 0.007$ km^2

1 mark for attempting to divide 2.1 by 3 and subtract the powers; 1 mark for correct answer in any form; 1 mark for correct answer as ordinary number including units. Total 3 marks.

Page 15, Simplifying expressions

1. a $y + 3x + y + x + 5y + x + 5y + x$

$= 12y + 6x$ (cm)

1 mark for adding up the lengths (allow mark if up to 2 missing terms); 1 mark for correct, simplified answer.

b $3xy + 5xy = 8xy$ (cm^2)

1 mark for multiplying to give either term; 1 mark for correct, simplified answer.

2. a $a^3 \times a^5 = a^8$

1 mark for correct answer.

b $a^3b^2 \div ab^3 = a^2b^{-1}$ or $\frac{a^2}{b}$

1 mark for power of either a or b terms correct; 1 mark for correct answer.

c $(2a^3b)^4 = 16a^{12}b^4$

1 mark for 16 or correct powers of a and b; 1 mark for correct answer.

d $\sqrt{9a^4b^2c^{-6}} = (9a^4b^2c^{-6})^{\frac{1}{2}}$

$= 3a^2bc^{-3}$ or $\frac{3a^2b}{c^3}$

1 mark for interpreting square root as power of $\frac{1}{2}$; 1 mark for correct answer.

Page 16, Solving linear equations

1. a $3x + 4x + 6 = 20 - 4x + 4x$

$7x + 6 - 6 = 20 - 6$

$\frac{7x}{7} = \frac{14}{7}$

$x = 2$

1 mark for adding $4x$ to both sides (or subtracting $3x$); 1 mark for correct answer.

b $\frac{x+6}{5} \times 5 = 8 \times 5$

$x + 6 - 6 = 40 - 6$

$x = 34$

1 mark for multiplying both sides by 5; 1 mark for correct answer.

c $\frac{3x}{4} - 3 + 3 = 9 + 3$

$\frac{3x}{4} \times 4 = 12 \times 4$

$\frac{3x}{3} = \frac{48}{3}$

$x = 16$

1 mark for multiplying both sides by 4 correctly (could have $3x - 12 = 36$ instead); 1 mark for correct answer.

2. Let Lucy's number be x

$4x + 15 = 5 - x$

$4x + x + 15 = 5 - x + x$

$5x + 15 - 15 = 5 - 15$

$\frac{5x}{5} = -\frac{10}{5}$

$x = -2$

1 mark for forming correct equation; 1 mark for adding x to both sides (or subtracting $4x$); 1 mark for correct answer. Total 3 marks.

Page 17, Linear graphs

1. Gradient $= 3$, equation is $y = 3x$

1 mark for correct gradient; 1 mark for correct equation.

2. a Gradient $= \frac{-2}{6} = -\frac{1}{3}$

1 mark for correct answer.

b Using points B and C to find gradient:

$\frac{a-(-7)}{7-4} = -\frac{1}{3}$

$a + 7 = -1$

$a = -8$

*1 mark for using gradient found in part **a**; 1 mark for correct answer.*

Page 18, Equations of linear graphs

1. a $2y = 10x - 1$ becomes $y = 5x - \frac{1}{2}$
which is parallel to $y = 5x + 1$
1 mark for rearranging one of the equations to make y the subject; 1 mark for correct answer.

b $2y + 1 = 5x$ becomes $y = \frac{5}{2}x - \frac{1}{2}$
which has the same y-intercept as $2y = 10x - 1$
$\left(y = 5x - \frac{1}{2}\right)$
1 mark for rearranging another equation to make y the subject; 1 mark for correct answer.

2. a $y = 5x - 3$
1 mark for correct answer.

b Gradient $= \frac{2}{4} = \frac{1}{2}$
$y = \frac{1}{2}x + 5$
1 mark for correct gradient; 1 mark for writing $y = mx + 5$ with your value of the gradient as m; 1 mark for correct answer. Total 3 marks.

c Gradient $= \frac{-2}{1} = -2$
$y = -2x + c$
Substitute in the point (1, 3): $3 = -2 \times 1 + c$
$\qquad\qquad\qquad\qquad\qquad 3 = -2 + c$
$\qquad\qquad\qquad\qquad\qquad c = 5$

$y = -2x + 5$
Alternatively:

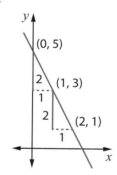

1 mark for correct gradient; 1 mark for attempting to find value of c, by either substituting into the equation or sketching part of the graph; 1 mark for writing $y = mx + c$ with your value of the gradient as m and your y-intercept as c; 1 mark for correct answer. Total 4 marks.

Page 19, Perpendicular lines

1. a $9y - 3x = 2$ becomes $y = \frac{3}{9}x + \frac{2}{9}$
y-intercept is $\frac{2}{9}$
1 mark for correct answer.

b i $y - \frac{1}{3}x = 4$ becomes $y = \frac{1}{3}x + 4$
Therefore, gradient is $\frac{1}{3}$, and from part **a**, gradient of L is $\frac{3}{9} = \frac{1}{3}$, so they are parallel.
1 mark for stating both gradients are $\frac{1}{3}$

ii $y + 3x = 4$ becomes $y = -3x + 4$
Gradient is -3
$-3 \times \frac{1}{3} = -1$, so this line is perpendicular to L
1 mark for identifying gradient as -3; 1 mark for showing product is -1 and conclusion.

2. a

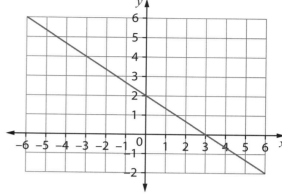

1 mark for line with negative gradient passing through (0, 2); 1 mark for correct answer.

b Gradient of L_2 is $\frac{3}{2}$
Equation is $y = \frac{3}{2}x + c$
Substitute in the point $(-8, 1)$:
$1 = \frac{3}{2}(-8) + c$
$1 = -12 + c$, so $c = 13$
Equation is $y = \frac{3}{2}x$ 13
1 mark for correct gradient of L_2; 1 mark for substituting coordinates; 1 mark for correct answer. Total 3 marks.

Page 20, Linear inequalities

1. a $x + 9 - 9 > 12 - 9$
$\qquad\qquad x > 3$

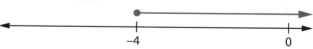

1 mark for correct solution (check you have the correct inequality sign); 1 mark for showing on number line (must have a hollow circle).

b $-3x + 3x \leq 12 + 3x$
$\qquad\qquad 0 \leq 12 + 3x$
$\qquad 0 - 12 \leq 12 - 12 + 3x$
$\qquad\qquad -12 \leq 3x$
$\qquad\qquad \frac{-12}{3} \leq \frac{3x}{3}$
$\qquad\qquad -4 \leq x$

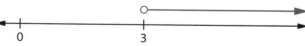

1 mark for subtracting 12 from both sides or adding 3x to both sides; 1 mark for correct solution (check you have the correct inequality sign); 1 mark for showing on number line (must have a filled-in circle). Total 3 marks.

c $2x + 13 - 13 \geq 25 - 13$
$$2x \geq 12$$
$$\frac{2x}{2} \geq \frac{12}{2}$$
$$x \geq 6$$

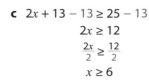

1 mark for rearranging correctly; 1 mark for correct solution (check you have the correct inequality sign); 1 mark for showing on number line (must have a filled-in circle). Total 3 marks.

2. a $x - 3 < 2x + 5$
$$-8 < x$$
$$12 - 5x > 7$$
$$5 > 5x$$
$$1 > x$$
$$\{x: -8 < x < 1\}$$

1 mark for correct solution to first inequality; 1 mark for correct solution to second inequality; 1 mark for correct range of values of x using your solutions; 1 mark for correct answer using set notation. Total 4 marks.

b

1 mark for correct answer (must be open circles).

c $-7, -6, -5, -4, -3, -2, -1, 0$

1 mark for all correct and no incorrect values.

Page 21, Regions on graphs

1. a $y \leq 4$

1 mark for $y \leq 4$ or $y < 4$; 1 mark for fully correct answer.

b $y < x$

1 mark for $y < x$ or $y \leq x$; 1 mark for fully correct answer.

2. a

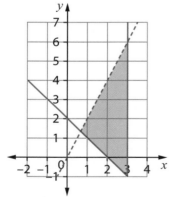

2 marks for 3 correct lines, or 1 mark for 2 correct lines; 1 mark for shading correct region. Total 3 marks.

b Nathan is incorrect since (2, 4) lies on the dotted line $y = 2x$

1 mark for correct answer with reason.

Page 22, Linear simultaneous equations

1. a $4x + 2y = 28$ (1) and $2x + 3y = 22$ (2)

1 mark for each correct equation.

b Multiply equation (2) by 2: $4x + 6y = 44$ (3)
(3) – (1): $4y = 16$
$$y = 4 \,\text{cm}$$
Substitute into equation (2): $2x + 12 = 22$
$$2x = 10$$
$$x = 5 \,\text{cm}$$

1 mark for correct equation in y or x; 1 mark for correct value of y or x; 1 mark for correct value of y and x including the units. Total 3 marks.

2. Using m = cost of bottle of milk, c = cost of pack of cheese:
$5m + 2c = 10.3$ (1) and $2m + 3c = 10.94$ (2)
Multiply equation (1) by 3: $15m + 6c = 30.9$ (3)
Multiply equation (2) by 2: $4m + 6c = 21.88$ (4)
(3) – (4): $11m = 9.02$
$$m = 0.82$$
Substitute into equation (2): $1.64 + 3c = 10.94$
$$3c = 9.3$$
$$c = 3.1$$
The cost of a bottle of milk is £0.82 (or 82p) and the cost of a pack of cheese is £3.10

1 mark for correct equations (you can use any two letters); 1 mark for multiplying equation (1) by 3 and equation (2) by 2 (or you could multiply equation (1) by 2 and equation (2) by 5 instead); 1 mark for correct value of m or c; 1 mark for correct cost of milk and cheese including units. Total 4 marks.

Page 23, Expanding brackets

1. Area $= x(y - 1) + (2x + 3)(y + 7)$
$$= xy - x + 2xy + 14x + 3y + 21$$
$$= 3xy + 13x + 3y + 21$$

1 mark for correct, unsimplified, expression for area; 1 mark for correct expansion of brackets; 1 mark for correct, fully simplified answer. Total 3 marks.

2. a $(3x + 2)(3x + 2) = 9x^2 + 6x + 6x + 4$
$$= 9x^2 + 12x + 4$$

1 mark for at least 3 correct terms; 1 mark for correct, simplified expression.

b $(2x - 1)(x + 1)(3x + 2)$
$$= (2x^2 + 2x - x - 1)(3x + 2)$$
$$= (2x^2 + x - 1)(3x + 2)$$
$$= 6x^3 + 4x^2 + 3x^2 + 2x - 3x - 2$$
$$= 6x^3 + 7x^2 - x - 2$$

1 mark for expanding first two brackets correctly (or final two to give $3x^2 + 5x + 2$); 1 mark for attempting to multiply this by third bracket (allow one error); 1 mark for correct, unsimplified expression; 1 mark for correct, simplified expression. Total 4 marks.

Page 24, Factorising 1

1. a $2x(3 - x)$

1 mark for correctly factorising with x or 2 outside brackets; 1 mark for fully factorised correct answer.

b $7a(2b + 3a)$

1 mark for correctly factorising with 7 or a outside brackets; 1 mark for fully factorised correct answer.

c $xy^2(z + z^2 + 1)$

1 mark for xy^2 outside bracket and at least two terms inside bracket correct; 1 mark for correct answer.

2. a $(x + 2)(x + 7)$

1 mark for correct answer.

b $(x + 10)(x - 2)$

1 mark for brackets with x and two numbers that multiply to give -20; *1 mark* for correct answer.

c $(x - 6)(x + 3)$

1 mark for brackets with x and two numbers that multiply to give -18; *1 mark* for correct answer.

d $(x - 9)(x - 1)$

1 mark for brackets with x and two numbers that multiply to give $+9$; *1 mark* for correct answer.

Page 25, Factorising 2

1. a $(x - 3)(x - 5)$

1 mark for brackets with x and two numbers that multiply to give $+15$; *1 mark* for correct answer.

b $12x(2 - x)$

1 mark for correct answer.

c $(x + 9y)(x - 9y)$

1 mark for correct answer.

2. a $5x^2 + 7x + 2 = 5x^2 + 5x + 2x + 2$
$$= 5x(x + 1) + 2(x + 1)$$
$$= (5x + 2)(x + 1)$$

1 mark for attempting to factorise by splitting x term or other method; *1 mark* for correct answer.

b $4x^2 - 21x - 18 = 4x^2 - 24x + 3x - 18$
$$= 4x(x - 6) + 3(x - 6)$$
$$= (4x + 3)(x - 6)$$

1 mark for attempting to factorise by splitting x term or other method; *1 mark* for correct answer.

c $10x^2 - 23x + 12 = 10x^2 - 8x - 15x + 12$
$$= 2x(5x - 4) - 3(5x - 4)$$
$$= (2x - 3)(5x - 4)$$

1 mark for attempting to factorise by splitting x term or other method; *1 mark* for correct answer.

Page 26, Solving quadratic equations

1. a $(x + 4)(x + 2) = 0$
$$x + 4 = 0 \text{ or } x + 2 = 0$$
$$x = -4 \text{ or } x = -2$$

1 mark for correctly factorising; *1 mark* for each correct value of x. Total 3 marks.

b $(x + 11)(x - 11) = 0$
$$x + 11 = 0 \text{ or } x - 11 = 0$$
$$x = -11 \text{ or } x = 11$$

1 mark for correctly factorising (or for writing down one correct answer); *1 mark* for both correct values of x

c $2x(x - 3) = 0$
$$2x = 0 \text{ or } x - 3 = 0$$
$$x = 0 \text{ or } x = 3$$

1 mark for correctly factorising; *1 mark* for each correct value of x. Total 3 marks.

d $x^2 + x - 12 = 0$
$$(x + 4)(x - 3) = 0$$
$$x + 4 = 0 \text{ or } x - 3 = 0$$
$$x = -4 \text{ or } x = 3$$

1 mark for rearranging to get zero on one side and factorising; *1 mark* for each correct value of x. Total 3 marks.

2. $5x^2 + 33x - 14 = 0$
$$5x^2 + 35x - 2x - 14 = 0$$
$$5x(x + 7) - 2(x + 7) = 0$$
$$(5x - 2)(x + 7) = 0$$
$$5x - 2 = 0 \text{ or } x + 7 = 0$$
$$x = \tfrac{2}{5} \text{ or } x = -7$$

1 mark for correct factorisation; *1 mark* for one correct solution from your factorisation (even if incorrect); *1 mark* for both correct solutions. Total 3 marks.

Page 27, The quadratic formula

1. a $x = \dfrac{-8 \pm \sqrt{8^2 - 4 \times 3 \times 3}}{2 \times 3}$

$x = -0.451 \text{ or } x = -2.22$

1 mark for writing out formula and attempting to substitute; *1 mark* for correct substitution; *1 mark* for both correct solutions. Total 3 marks.

b $x = \dfrac{-(-8) \pm \sqrt{(-8)^2 - 4 \times 5 \times 1}}{2 \times 5}$

$x = 1.46 \text{ or } x = 0.137$

1 mark for writing out formula and attempting to substitute; *1 mark* for correct substitution; *1 mark* for both correct solutions. Total 3 marks.

2. $x = \dfrac{-2 \pm \sqrt{2^2 - 4 \times 1 \times (-7)}}{2 \times 1}$

$= \dfrac{-2 \pm \sqrt{32}}{2}$

$= \dfrac{-2 \pm 4\sqrt{2}}{2}$

$= -1 \pm 2\sqrt{2}$

$(a = -1, b = 2)$

1 mark for writing out formula and attempting to substitute; *1 mark* for correct substitution; *1 mark* for simplifying surd correctly; *1 mark* for correct answer in form $a \pm b\sqrt{2}$. Total 4 marks.

Page 28, Completing the square

1. a i $(x + 7)^2$ **ii** $(x + 7)^2 - 49$

iii $(x + 7)^2 - 27$

1 mark for each correct answer. Total 3 marks.

b $(x + 7)^2 - 27 = 0$
$$(x + 7)^2 = 27$$
$$x + 7 = \pm\sqrt{27}$$
$$= \pm 3\sqrt{3}$$
$$x = -7 \pm 3\sqrt{3}$$

1 mark for using $(x + 7)^2 = 27$; *1 mark* for finding square root of both sides (only need positive square root for this mark) and subtracting 7; *1 mark* for both correct solutions in surd form. Total 3 marks.

2. a $2x^2 + 5x = 2\left[x^2 + \tfrac{5}{2}x\right]$
$$= 2\left[\left(x + \tfrac{5}{4}\right)^2 - \tfrac{25}{16}\right]$$
$$= 2\left(x + \tfrac{5}{4}\right)^2 - \tfrac{25}{8}$$
$$2x^2 + 5x + 10 = 2\left(x + \tfrac{5}{4}\right)^2 - \tfrac{25}{8} + 10$$
$$= 2\left(x + \tfrac{5}{4}\right)^2 + \tfrac{55}{8}$$

1 mark for removing factor of 2 and correct constant in squared bracket; *1 mark* for subtracting your constant squared; *1 mark* for correct answer. Total 3 marks.

b $-x^2 + 4x = -[x^2 - 4x]$
$$= -[(x - 2)^2 - 4]$$
$$= -(x - 2)^2 + 4$$
$$-x^2 + 4x - 7 = -(x - 2)^2 + 4 - 7$$
$$= -(x - 2)^2 - 3$$

*1 mark for removing factor of −1 and correct constant in squared bracket; **1 mark** for subtracting your constant squared; **1 mark** for correct answer. Total 3 marks.*

Page 29, Algebraic fractions 1

1. a $\frac{15x^3}{18x} = \frac{5x^2}{6}$

1 mark for correct answer.

b $\frac{6x(x + 2)}{12x^2(x - 2)} = \frac{x + 2}{2x(x - 2)}$

*1 mark for cancelling common factor of 6 or x; **1 mark** for correct answer (if you try to simplify it further than this then you cannot score the second mark).*

c $\frac{x^2 - 7x}{x^2 - 6x - 7} = \frac{x(x - 7)}{(x - 7)(x + 1)}$
$$= \frac{x}{x + 1}$$

*1 mark for factorising numerator; **1 mark** for factorising denominator; **1 mark** for correct answer. Total 3 marks.*

d $\frac{2x^2 - x - 1}{(x^2 - 1)} = \frac{(2x + 1)(x - 1)}{(x + 1)(x - 1)}$
$$= \frac{2x + 1}{x + 1}$$

*1 mark for factorising numerator; **1 mark** for factorising denominator; **1 mark** for correct simplification. Total 3 marks.*

2. a $\frac{2x^2 - 9x - 5}{3x^2 - 15x} = \frac{(2x + 1)(x - 5)}{3x(x - 5)}$
$$= \frac{2x + 1}{3x}$$

*1 mark for factorising numerator; **1 mark** for factorising denominator; **1 mark** for correct answer. Total 3 marks.*

b $\frac{2x + 1}{3x} = x$
$$2x + 1 = 3x^2$$
$$3x^2 - 2x - 1 = 0$$
$$(3x + 1)(x - 1) = 0$$
$$3x + 1 = 0 \text{ or } x - 1 = 0$$
$$x = -\frac{1}{3} \text{ or } x = 1$$

*1 mark for using your simplified equation from part **a** and multiplying both sides by the denominator of this fraction; **1 mark** for rearranging so that one side of the equation is 0; **1 mark** for factorising this expression correctly (or using other method to solve a quadratic); **1 mark** for both correct answers. Total 4 marks.*

Page 30, Algebraic fractions 2

1. a $\frac{3x}{x + 2} \times \frac{2}{3x^2 + 6x} = \frac{3x}{x + 2} \times \frac{2}{3x(x + 2)}$
$$= \frac{6x}{3x(x + 2)^2}$$
$$= \frac{2}{(x + 2)^2}$$

*1 mark for factorising denominator; **1 mark** for multiplying numerators and denominators; **1 mark** for correct answer $\left(\text{allow } \frac{2}{(x + 2)(x + 2)}\right)$. Total 3 marks.*

b $\frac{2x^3 - 18x}{x^2 - 2x - 3} \div \frac{4x + 12}{x + 1} = \frac{2x(x^2 - 9)}{(x - 3)(x + 1)} \times \frac{x + 1}{4(x + 3)}$
$$= \frac{2x(x + 3)(x - 3)(x + 1)}{4(x - 3)(x + 1)(x + 3)}$$
$$= \frac{x}{2}$$

*1 mark for writing as a multiplication; **1 mark** for factorising $x^2 - 2x - 3$; **1 mark** for factorising $2x^3 - 18x$ fully; **1 mark** for cancelling at least two common factors; **1 mark** for correct answer. Total 5 marks.*

2. $\frac{2}{x^2 + 5} = \frac{1}{3x}$
$$6x = x^2 + 5$$
$$x^2 - 6x + 5 = 0$$
$$(x - 5)(x - 1) = 0$$
$$x = 1 \text{ or } x = 5$$

*1 mark for forming a correct equation involving an algebraic fraction (could also have $2 = \frac{x^2 + 5}{3x}$ or $\frac{x^2 + 5}{2} = 3x$); **1 mark** for writing as a quadratic equation; **1 mark** for method to solve quadratic equation; **1 mark** for both correct answers. Total 4 marks.*

Page 31, Algebraic fractions 3

1. a $\frac{x}{2} + \frac{x}{5} = \frac{5x}{10} + \frac{2x}{10} = \frac{7x}{10}$

*1 mark for writing over common denominator; **1 mark** for correct answer.*

b $\frac{x + 2}{2} - \frac{x - 1}{4} = \frac{2(x + 2)}{4} - \frac{x - 1}{4}$
$$= \frac{2x + 4 - x + 1}{4} = \frac{x + 5}{4}$$

*1 mark for writing over common denominator; **1 mark** for correct (unsimplified) fraction (equivalent fractions allowed); **1 mark** for correct answer. Total 3 marks.*

c $\frac{1}{x + 5} + \frac{2}{x - 3} = \frac{x - 3}{(x + 5)(x - 3)} + \frac{2(x + 5)}{(x + 5)(x - 3)}$
$$= \frac{x - 3 + 2x + 10}{(x + 5)(x - 3)}$$
$$= \frac{3x + 7}{(x + 5)(x - 3)}$$

*1 mark for writing over common denominator; **1 mark** for correct (unsimplified) fraction; **1 mark** for correct answer. Total 3 marks.*

d $\frac{2}{x + 1} - \frac{1}{2x - 1} = \frac{2(2x - 1)}{(x + 1)(2x - 1)} - \frac{x + 1}{(x + 1)(2x - 1)}$
$$= \frac{4x - 2 - x - 1}{(x + 1)(2x - 1)}$$
$$= \frac{3x - 3}{(x + 1)(2x - 1)} \text{ or } \frac{3(x - 1)}{(x + 1)(2x - 1)}$$

*1 mark for writing over common denominator; **1 mark** for correct (unsimplified) fraction; **1 mark** for correct answer. Total 3 marks.*

2. a $\frac{1}{3x - 1} - \frac{2}{9x^2 - 1} = \frac{1}{3x - 1} - \frac{2}{(3x + 1)(3x - 1)}$
$$= \frac{(3x + 1) - 2}{(3x + 1)(3x - 1)}$$
$$= \frac{3x - 1}{(3x + 1)(3x - 1)}$$
$$= \frac{1}{3x + 1} \quad (a = 3, b = 1)$$

*1 mark for factorising $9x^2 - 1$; **1 mark** for writing over common denominator; **1 mark** for correct (unsimplified) fraction; **1 mark** for correct answer. Total 4 marks.*

b $\frac{1}{3x+1} = 1 - x$

$1 = (3x+1)(1-x)$

$1 = -3x^2 + 2x + 1$

$3x^2 - 2x = 0$

$x(3x-2) = 0$

$x = 0$ or $x = \frac{2}{3}$

*1 mark for using answer to part **a** and multiplying both sides of equation by the denominator; **1 mark** for correct method of solving quadratic; **1 mark** for each correct answer. Total 4 marks.*

Page 32, Rearranging formulae

1. a $E \times 2 = \frac{1}{2}ms^2 \times 2$

$\frac{2E}{m} = \frac{ms^2}{m}$

$s^2 = \frac{2E}{m}$

$s = \sqrt{\frac{2E}{m}}$

*1 mark for multiplying both sides by 2; **1 mark** for dividing both sides by m; **1 mark** for final answer. Total 3 marks.*

b $s = \sqrt{\frac{2 \times 8}{4}} = \sqrt{4} = 2$

*1 mark for substituting into the rearranged formula found in part **a** (or into the original formula); **1 mark** for correct answer.*

2. $x + 2 = \frac{5-x}{y}$

$xy + 2y = 5 - x$

$xy + x = 5 - 2y$

$x(y+1) = 5 - 2y$

$x = \frac{5-2y}{y+1}$

*1 mark for multiplying both sides by y; **1 mark** for moving x terms to one side and factorising; **1 mark** for correct answer. Total 3 marks.*

Page 33, Quadratic graphs 1

1. a

x	-2	-1	0	1	2
y	4	-2	-4	-2	4

*1 mark for at least two correct values; **1 mark** for all values correct.*

b

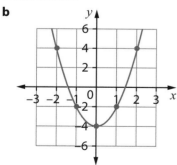

*1 mark for plotting values from table; **1 mark** for correct points joined with a smooth curve.*

2. a Turning point is $(-2, 3)$.

1 mark for correct answer.

b Roots are approximately $x = -3.7$ and $x = -0.3$

1 mark for each root. Allow 0.1 either side (e.g. between −3.8 and −3.6, and between −0.4 and −0.2 respectively).

Page 34, Quadratic graphs 2

1. a

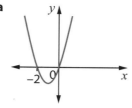

*1 mark for correct shape; **1 mark** for x-intercepts.*

b

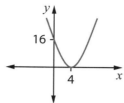

*1 mark for correct shape; **1 mark** for touching x-axis once at 4; **1 mark** for y-intercept. Total 3 marks.*

c

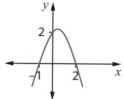

*1 mark for correct shape; **1 mark** for x-intercepts; **1 mark** for y-intercept. Total 3 marks.*

d

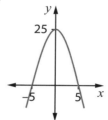

*1 mark for correct shape; **1 mark** for x-intercepts; **1 mark** for y-intercept. Total 3 marks.*

2. a $f(x) = x^2 + x + 1 = \left(x + \frac{1}{2}\right)^2 - \frac{1}{4} + 1$

$= \left(x + \frac{1}{2}\right)^2 + \frac{3}{4}$

Turning point is at $\left(-\frac{1}{2}, \frac{3}{4}\right)$

*1 mark for attempting to complete the square with $\frac{1}{2}$ inside bracket; **1 mark** for correctly completing the square; **1 mark** for correct x- or y-coordinate from your completed square form; **1 mark** for coordinates both correct. Total 4 marks.*

b

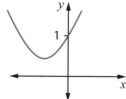

*1 mark for correct shape; **1 mark** for y-intercept; **1 mark** for turning point in correct quadrant. Total 3 marks.*

c The graph of $y = f(x)$ does not cross the x-axis, so $f(x)$ does not have any real roots.

*1 mark for reason; **1 mark** for conclusion.*

Page 35, Quadratic inequalities

1. a $-3 < x < 3$

1 mark for correct answer.

b $5x^2 > 80$

$x^2 > 16$

$x < -4, x > 4$

1 mark for finding $x > 4$; *1 mark* for fully correct answer (must be written as two separate inequalities).

c $4x^2 + 7 \leq 15$

$4x^2 \leq 8$

$x^2 \leq 2$

$-\sqrt{2} \leq x \leq \sqrt{2}$

1 mark for finding $x^2 \leq 2$; *1 mark* for writing $x \leq \sqrt{2}$; *1 mark* for fully correct answer. Total 3 marks.

2. a Write as an equation:

$x^2 - 7x + 10 = 0$

$(x - 5)(x - 2) = 0$

$x = 5$ or $x = 2$

Solution: $2 < x < 5$

In set notation $\{x : 2 < x < 4\}$

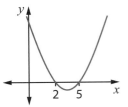

1 mark for method, i.e. solving quadratic equation; *1 mark* for finding correct solutions to equation; *1 mark* for sketching graph or other method for solving inequality; *1 mark* for correct solution in set notation. Total 4 marks.

b $3x^2 - 2x \geq 1$ becomes

$3x^2 - 2x - 1 \geq 0$

Write as an equation:

$3x^2 - 2x - 1 = 0$

$3x^2 - 3x + x - 1 = 0$

$3x(x - 1) + (x - 1) = 0$

$(3x + 1)(x - 1) = 0$

$x = -\frac{1}{3}$ or $x = 1$

Solution: $x \leq -\frac{1}{3}, x \geq 1$

In set notation $\{x : x \leq -\frac{1}{3}$ or $x \geq 1\}$

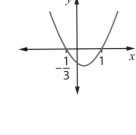

1 mark for method, i.e. solving quadratic equation; *1 mark* for finding correct solutions to equation; *1 mark* for sketching graph or other method for solving inequality; *1 mark* for correct solution in set notation (must be written as two separate inequalities). Total 4 marks.

c $x^2 + 4x + 1 = 0$

Complete the square:

$(x + 2)^2 - 3 = 0$

$(x + 2)^2 = 3$

$x + 2 = \pm\sqrt{3}$

$x = -2 \pm \sqrt{3}$

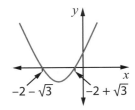

(Or you could use quadratic formula.)

$-2 - \sqrt{3} \leq x \leq -2 + \sqrt{3}$

In set notation $\{x : -2 - \sqrt{3} \leq x \leq -2 + \sqrt{3}\}$

1 mark for method, i.e. solving quadratic equation; *1 mark* for finding correct solutions to equation; *1 mark* for sketching graph or other method for solving inequality; *1 mark* for correct solution in set notation. Total 4 marks.

Page 36, Non-linear simultaneous equations

1. a $x = 6 - y$

$(6 - y)^2 - y^2 = 144$

$36 - 12y + y^2 - y^2 = 144$

$-12y = 108$

$y = -9$

$x = 6 - (-9) = 15$

1 mark for rearranging linear equation and substituting into quadratic equation; *1 mark* for simplifying to a linear equation and attempting to solve; *1 mark* for solution for y; *1 mark* for solution for x. Total 4 marks.

b $x = y - 2$

$y - 2 + y^2 = 0$

$y^2 + y - 2 = 0$

$(y + 2)(y - 1) = 0$

$y = -2$ or $y = 1$

When $y = -2$, $x = (-2) - 2 = -4$

When $y = 1$, $x = 1 - 2 = -1$

1 mark for substituting for x or y in the quadratic equation and attempting to solve; *1 mark* for correct solutions for either x or y; *1 mark* for substituting to find correct solutions for other variable; *1 mark* for all solutions correct. Total 4 marks.

c $y = 19 - 2x$

$x^2 - x(19 - 2x) = 14$

$x^2 - 19x + 2x^2 = 14$

$3x^2 - 19x - 14 = 0$

$3x^2 - 21x + 2x - 14 = 0$

$3x(x - 7) + 2(x - 7) = 0$

$(3x + 2)(x - 7) = 0$

$x = -\frac{2}{3}$ or $x = 7$

When $x = -\frac{2}{3}, y = 19 - 2\left(-\frac{2}{3}\right) = \frac{61}{3}$

When $x = 7$, $y = 19 - 2(7) = 5$

1 mark for substituting for x or y in the quadratic equation and attempting to solve; *1 mark* for correct solutions for either x or y; *1 mark* for substituting to find correct solutions for other variable; *1 mark* for all solutions correct. Total 4 marks.

2. C has equation $x^2 + y^2 = 5$

Need to find point of intersection with tangent:

$x - 2y + 5 = 0$

$x = 2y - 5$

Substitute in equation of C:

$(2y - 5)^2 + y^2 = 5$

$4y^2 - 20y + 25 + y^2 = 5$

$5y^2 - 20y + 20 = 0$

$y^2 - 4y + 4 = 0$

$(y - 2)^2 = 0$

$y = 2$

$x = 2(2) - 5 = -1$

A has coordinates $(-1, 2)$.

1 mark for correct equation of C; *1 mark* for rearranging linear equation and substituting into equation of C; *1 mark* for method to solve quadratic equation; *1 mark* for correct solution for either x or y; *1 mark* for substituting to find correct solution for other variable; *1 mark* for correct answer as coordinates. Total 6 marks.

Page 37, Solutions from graphs

1.

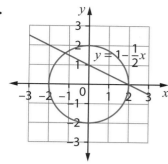

$x = 2, y = 0$ and $x = -1.2, y = 1.6$

*1 mark for adding line $y = 1 - \frac{1}{2}x$ onto graph; **1 mark** for one correct solution pair; **1 mark** for both solutions correct (allow 0.1 either side for $x = -1.2, y = 1.6$). Total 3 marks.*

2. $x^3 + x^2 + 3x = 1$ becomes
$x^3 + x^2 + x = 1 - 2x$

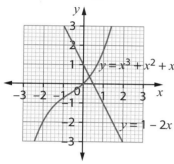

Where they intersect, $x = 0.3$ to 1 decimal place.

*1 mark for working out correct line to draw; **1 mark** for adding line onto graph; **1 mark** for correct solution to 1 decimal place. Total 3 marks.*

Page 38, Cubic and reciprocal graphs

1. a

x	-2	-1	0	1	2
y	-16	-2	0	2	16

*1 mark for at least two correct values; **1 mark** for all values correct.*

b

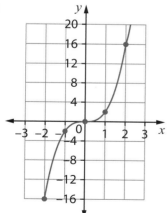

*1 mark for plotting values from table; **1 mark** for joining with smooth curve.*

2. Reciprocal graph, so $y = \frac{A}{x}$
Using point $(-1, 2)$:
$2 = \frac{A}{-1} \Rightarrow A = -2$
Equation is $y = -\frac{2}{x}$

*1 mark for any reciprocal equation; **1 mark** for correct equation.*

Page 39, Exponential graphs

1. a i $y = -\frac{2}{x}$ **ii** $y = 2^x$

1 mark for each correct answer circled.

b

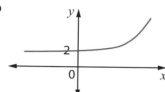

*1 mark for shape of graph; **1 mark** for completely correct sketch including the y-intercept.*

2. a 10%

1 mark for correct answer.

b $4370 = A \times 0.9^3$

$A = \frac{4370}{0.9^3}$

$= 5994.513\ldots = 5990$ (to 3 sf)

*1 mark for substituting into the equation; **1 mark** for correct value to 3 significant figures.*

Page 40, Equation of a circle

1. a Radius $= \sqrt{18}$ $(= 3\sqrt{2})$

1 mark for correct answer.

b $a^2 + 4^2 = 18$

$a^2 = 2$

$a = \pm\sqrt{2}$

*1 mark for substituting into equation of circle and attempting to solve for a; **1 mark** for correct solutions (need both).*

2. Gradient of radius $= \frac{-\sqrt{5}}{-5} = \frac{\sqrt{5}}{5}$

Gradient of tangent $= -\frac{5}{\sqrt{5}} = -\sqrt{5}$

Substitute coordinates of point and gradient into equation:

$-\sqrt{5} = -\sqrt{5}(-5) + c$

$-\sqrt{5} = 5\sqrt{5} + c$

$c = -6\sqrt{5}$

Equation is $y = -\sqrt{5}x - 6\sqrt{5}$

*1 mark for gradient of radius; **1 mark** for gradient of tangent as negative reciprocal of your gradient of radius; **1 mark** for substituting your values to find value of c; **1 mark** for correct value of c; **1 mark** for final equation. Total 5 marks.*

Page 41, Trigonometric graphs

a

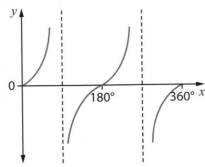

1 mark for correct shape and passing through origin; *1 mark* for completely correct including x-intercepts labelled.

b Graph repeats every 180° so, e.g.
$\theta = 60 + 180 = 240°$
(or −120°, −300°, etc.)
1 mark for any correct value.

c $x = 80°$
1 mark for correct answer.

Page 42, Graph transformations 1

1. a $(0, -2)$
1 mark for correct answer.

b $(3, -5)$
1 mark for 3; *1 mark* for −5

2.

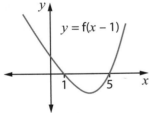

1 mark for a horizontal translation; *1 mark* for fully correct translation with x-intercepts labelled.

Page 43, Graph transformations 2

1. a $(1, 2)$ **b** $(-1, -2)$
1 mark for each correct answer.

2.

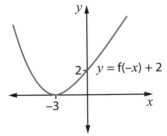

1 mark for reflecting graph in y-axis; *1 mark* for translating up 2 units (so that graph just touches x-axis); *1 mark* for completely correct including x-intercept labelled. Total 3 marks.

Page 44, Simple kinematic graphs

a Acceleration $= \frac{12}{2} = 6\,\text{m/s}^2$
1 mark for attempting to calculate the gradient; *1 mark* for correct answer.

b Area under graph $= \frac{1}{2} \times 12 \times T = 108$
$6T = 108$
$T = 18$
1 mark for using area under graph; *1 mark* for correct answer.

Page 45, Estimating areas

a $A_1 = \frac{1}{2} \times (0.8 + 1.8) \times 1 = 1.3$
$A_2 = \frac{1}{2} \times (1.8 + 3.2) \times 1 = 2.5$
$A_3 = \frac{1}{2} \times (3.2 + 5) \times 1 = 4.1$
Total area under graph $\approx 1.3 + 2.5 + 4.1 = 7.9$
1 mark for starting to find areas of trapeziums, using at least two of 0.8, 1.8, 3.2 or 5; *1 mark* for finding at least two correct areas; *1 mark* for correct final answer (between 7.8 and 8.0). Total 3 marks.

b Distance in metres covered by the object
1 mark for distance; *1 mark* for metres.

c Over-estimate, as chords are above the curve.
1 mark for correct answer and explanation.

Page 46, Rates of change

1. a Fixed fee $= £50$
1 mark for correct answer.

b Choose two points, e.g. (0, 50) and (2, 140).
Gradient $= \frac{\text{change in } y}{\text{change in } x} = \frac{90}{2} = 45$
Cost per day $= £45$
1 mark for using correct rule to calculate gradient; *1 mark* for correct answer.

2. a   **b**

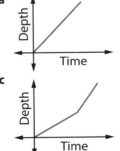
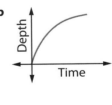

c

1 mark for each correct graph. Total 3 marks.

Page 47, Gradients of curves

For a triangle using (0, 0) and (2, 6),
gradient of tangent $= \frac{6}{2} = 3$
Acceleration $\approx 3\,\text{m/s}^2$
1 mark for attempting to calculate an appropriate gradient; *1 mark* for correct answer.

Page 48, Types of sequence

1. a 9th term = $100 - 7 \times 9 = 100 - 63 = 37$

1 mark for correct answer.

b $100 - 7n < 0$

$100 < 7n$

$n > \frac{100}{7} = 14\frac{2}{7}$

The first negative term is the 15th term:

15th term = $100 - 7 \times 15 = -5$

Or, write out the sequence (could start at 9th term as found in part **a**):

(93, 86, 79, 72, 65, 58, 51, 44, 37,) 30, 23, 16, 9, 2, −5

The first negative term is −5

1 mark for solving inequality or for writing out the sequence; 1 mark for correct answer.

c $100 - 7n = 50$; $7n = 50$

50 is not a multiple of 7, so the solution is not an integer.

Therefore, 50 is not a term in the sequence.

1 mark for attempting to solve $100 - 7n = 50$; 1 mark for correct answer with explanation.

2. Geometric, so $12 \times r = 4$

$r = \frac{1}{3}$ (or ÷ 3)

2nd term = $108 \times \frac{1}{3} = 36$

5th term = $4 \times \frac{1}{3} = \frac{4}{3}$

1 mark for finding the number to multiply by each time; 1 mark for both terms correct.

Page 49, Arithmetic sequences

1. a Common difference = −2

−2n: −2 −4 −6 −8 −10
     +7   +7   +7   +7   +7
     5   3   1   −1   −3

The nth term is $-2n + 7$ (or $7 - 2n$)

1 mark for a rule involving −2n; 1 mark for fully correct answer.

b Common difference = $1\frac{1}{2}$ or 1.5

$1\frac{1}{2}n$: $1\frac{1}{2}$ 3 $4\frac{1}{2}$ 6 $7\frac{1}{2}$
        −1   −1   −1   −1   −1
        $\frac{1}{2}$ 2 $3\frac{1}{2}$ 5 $6\frac{1}{2}$

The nth term is $1\frac{1}{2}n - 1$ (or $1.5n - 1$)

1 mark for a rule involving $1\frac{1}{2}n$ or 1.5n; 1 mark for fully correct answer.

2. a Amount paid in = $7m + 23$

1 mark for rule involving 7m; 1 mark for fully correct answer.

b December is 12th month.

12th term = $7 \times 12 + 23 = £107$

1 mark for substituting m = 12 into expression found in part a; 1 mark for correct answer.

Page 50, Quadratic sequences

1. Number of squares = $n(n + 1)$ (or $n^2 + n$)

1 mark for rule involving n^2; 1 mark for correct answer.

2. a

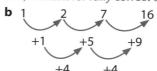

Rule involves n^2:

	1	5	11	19
$-n^2$:	1	4	9	16
	0	1	2	3

nth term of linear sequence is $n - 1$

nth term of quadratic sequence is $n^2 + n - 1$

1 mark for finding coefficient of n^2; 1 mark for coefficient of n; 1 mark for fully correct answer. Total 3 marks.

b 1 2 7 16
    +1   +5   +9
    +4   +4

Rule involves $2n^2$:

	1	2	7	16
$-2n^2$:	2	8	18	32
	−1	−6	−11	−16

nth term of linear sequence is $-5n + 4$

nth term of quadratic sequence is $2n^2 - 5n + 4$

1 mark for finding coefficient of n^2; 1 mark for coefficient of n; 1 mark for fully correct answer. Total 3 marks.

Page 51, Iteration 1

1. a Rearrange to give $x^3 + x^2 - 5 = 0$

Substitute $x = 1$: $1^3 + 1^2 - 5 = -3$

Substitute $x = 2$: $2^3 + 2^2 - 5 = 7$

Change of sign, therefore solution between $x = 1$ and $x = 2$

1 mark for rearranging and substituting in values; 1 mark for both values correct and conclusion.

b $x_1 = \sqrt{\frac{5}{1+1}} = 1.5811... = 1.58$ (3 sf)

$x_2 = \sqrt{\frac{5}{1.58... + 1}} = 1.3918... = 1.38$ (3 sf)

1 mark for each correct answer.

2. $x_1 = 2 + \frac{1}{2^2} = \frac{9}{4}$, $x_2 = 2.1975...$,

$x_3 = 2.2070...$, $x_4 = 2.2052...$,

$x_5 = 2.2056...$

Solution is $x = 2.21$ to 3 significant figures.

1 mark for substituting into formula to find x_1; 1 mark for finding x_4 or higher; 1 mark for correct answer. Total 3 marks.

Page 52, Iteration 2

a Substitute in $x = 1$: $2(1)^3 + 1 - 4 = -1$

Substitute in $x = 2$: $2(2)^3 + 2 - 4 = 14$

Since there's a change of sign, there must be a root between $x = 1$ and $x = 2$

1 mark for substituting both x values; 1 mark for both values correct and conclusion.

b $2x^3 + x - 4 = 0$

$$2x^3 = 4 - x$$
$$x^3 = \frac{4 - x}{2}$$
$$x = \sqrt[3]{\frac{4 - x}{2}}$$

1 mark for arranging to make x^3 the subject; 1 mark for complete proof.

c Iteration formula is $x_{n+1} = \sqrt[3]{\frac{4 - x_n}{2}}$

$$x_1 = \sqrt[3]{\frac{4 - 1}{2}} = 1.1447\ldots$$

$$x_2 = 1.1260\ldots$$

$x = 1.1$ to 2 significant figures

1 mark for substituting into formula; 1 mark for correct values of x_1 and x_2; 1 mark for answer given to 2 significant figures. Total 3 marks.

Page 53, Functions

1. a $f(7) = \frac{7 + 1}{4} = 2$

1 mark for correct answer.

b $\frac{x + 1}{4} = 5$

$x + 1 = 20, x = 19$

1 mark for setting f(x) equal to 5 and attempting to solve; 1 mark for correct answer.

2. a $f(5) = (-5)^2 - 2 = 23$

1 mark for correct answer.

b $fg(x) = f(2x + 1) = (2x + 1)^2 - 2$

$$= 4x^2 + 4x + 1 - 2$$
$$= 4x^2 + 4x - 1$$

1 mark for substituting g(x) into f(x); 1 mark for correct proof.

c $gf(x) = g(x^2 - 2) = 2(x^2 - 2) + 1$

$$= 2x^2 - 4 + 1$$
$$= 2x^2 - 3$$

Solve $4x^2 + 4x - 1 = 2x^2 - 3$

$$2x^2 + 4x + 2 = 0$$
$$x^2 + 2x + 1 = 0$$
$$(x + 1)^2 = 0$$
$$x = -1$$

1 mark for $2x^2 - 3$; 1 mark for setting equal to your answer from part b and attempting to solve; 1 mark for correct answer. Total 3 marks.

Page 54, Inverse functions

1. a Let $y = 11 + 3x$

$$3x = y - 11$$
$$x = \frac{y - 11}{3}$$
$$f^{-1}(x) = \frac{x - 11}{3}$$

1 mark for attempting to rearrange; 1 mark for correct answer using correct notation.

b Let $y = 11 - \frac{3}{x}$

$$\frac{3}{x} = 11 - y$$
$$\frac{x}{3} = \frac{1}{11 - y}$$
$$x = \frac{3}{11 - y}$$
$$g^{-1}(x) = \frac{3}{11 - x}$$

1 mark for attempting to rearrange (at least two correct steps); 1 mark for correct answer using correct notation.

c Let $y = \frac{11 - 3x}{x}$

$$yx = 11 - 3x$$
$$yx + 3x = 11$$
$$x(y + 3) = 11$$
$$x = \frac{11}{y + 3}$$
$$h^{-1}(x) = \frac{11}{x + 3}$$

1 mark for multiplying both sides by x; 1 mark for factorising one side; 1 mark for correct answer using correct notation. Total 3 marks.

2. a $g(7) = 49 - 7k$

$$7 = 49 - 7k$$
$$7k = 42, k = 6$$

1 mark for correct expression for g(7); 1 mark for correct answer.

b Let $y = x^2 - 6x$

$$= (x - 3)^2 - 9$$
$$y + 9 = (x - 3)^2$$
$$\sqrt{y + 9} = x - 3$$
$$3 + \sqrt{y + 9} = x$$
$$g^{-1}(x) = 3 + \sqrt{x + 9}$$

1 mark for completing the square; 1 mark for rearranging correctly, up to the square root; 1 mark for answer using correct notation. Total 3 marks.

Page 55, Algebraic proof

1. a e.g. let $a = -1$ and $b = -2$

Then $a > b$ since $-1 > -2$

but $a^2 \not> b^2$ since $1 < 4$

1 mark for picking two numbers that satisfy $a > b$ but not $a^2 > b^2$; 1 mark for full explanation.

b $(3n + 2)^2 - (3n + 1)^2$

$$\equiv (9n^2 + 12n + 4) - (9n^2 + 6n + 1)$$
$$\equiv 6n + 3$$
$$\equiv 3(2n + 1)$$

which is a multiple of 3

1 mark for expanding brackets correctly; 1 mark for correct simplification; 1 mark for factorising and conclusion. Total 3 marks.

2. Let n and m be positive integers, then $2n + 1$ and $2m + 1$ are odd numbers.

Product $= (2n + 1)(2m + 1)$

$$\equiv 4mn + 2n + 2m + 1$$
$$\equiv 2(2mn + n + m) + 1$$

which is an odd number because $2(2mn + n + m)$ is an even number.

1 mark for defining two odd numbers; 1 mark for correct product; 1 mark for full proof including conclusion. Total 3 marks.

Page 56, Ratio

1. $27 \div (1 + 2 + 3) = 4.5$

Amount of water $= 4.5$ kg

Amount of cement $= 2 \times 4.5 = 9$ kg

Amount of sand $= 3 \times 4.5 = 13.5$ kg

1 mark for working out that 1 part is 4.5; 1 mark for finding correct amounts of two of the ingredients; 1 mark for all three quantities correct. Total 3 marks.

2. Ratio flour:sugar = 3:1 = 6:2
So, flour:sugar:butter = 6:2:5
$26 \div (6 + 2 + 5) = 2\,g$
Amount of butter for 1 biscuit = $5 \times 2 = 10\,g$
Amount of butter for 12 biscuits = $10 \times 12 = 120\,g$
1 mark for finding correct 3-part ratio; 1 mark for working out that 1 part is 2 g; 1 mark for finding amount of butter for 1 biscuit; 1 mark for correct final answer. Total 4 marks.

Page 57, Harder ratio problems

1. $x:y = 3:4$ and $y:z = 2:3 = 4:6$
$x:y:z = 3:4:6$
1 mark for correct ratio $x:y$; 1 mark for correct ratio $y:z$; 1 mark for correct answer in simplest form. Total 3 marks.

2. $m:c = 2:1$
$\Rightarrow m = 2c$ $\qquad$ (1)
$(m - 50):(c + 50) = 3:2$
$\Rightarrow \dfrac{m - 50}{c + 50} = \dfrac{3}{2}$
$2m - 100 = 3c + 150$
$2m - 3c = 250$ $\qquad$ (2)
Substitute **(1)** into **(2)**:
$2(2c) - 3c = 250$
$\qquad c = 250\,ml$
$m = 2 \times 250 = 500\,ml$
The original recipe has 250 ml of cream and 500 ml of milk.
1 mark for correct equation involving m and c and no ratios; 1 mark for both correct equations involving m and c and no ratios; 1 mark for attempting to solve simultaneously; 1 mark for correct quantity of milk; 1 mark for correct quantity of cream. Total 5 marks.

Page 58, Percentage change

1. 10% of £25 is £2.50
40% of £25 is £2.50 × 4 = £10
Cost for child = £25 − £10 = £15
1 mark for attempting to find 40% and subtracting your answer from £25; 1 mark for correct answer.
Alternatively:
10% of £25 is £2.50
60% of £25 is 6 × £2.50 = £15
1 mark for attempting to find 60%; 1 mark for correct answer.

2. Percentage increase = $\dfrac{0.33}{2.2} \times 100\% = 15\%$
1 mark for correct answer circled.

Page 59, Using multipliers

1. 100% − 30% = 70% = 0.7
196 ÷ 0.7 = 280 seconds
1 mark for dividing by 0.7; 1 mark for correct answer.

2. 100% + 5% = 105% = 1.05
100% + 8% = 108% = 1.08
670 ÷ 1.08 ÷ 1.05 = £591 to the nearest £
1 mark for at least one multiplier correct; 1 mark for dividing by 1.08 or 1.05; 1 mark for correct answer. Total 3 marks.

Page 60, Growth and depreciation

1. $32\,000 \times 1.03^{10} = 43\,000$ to the nearest 1000
1 mark for correct multiplier; 1 mark for using correct formula; 1 mark for correct answer rounded to an integer. Total 3 marks.

2. Value after 1 year = 400 × 0.7 = £280
Value after 3 years = 200
$280 \times (\text{multiplier})^2 = 200$
$\qquad (\text{multiplier})^2 = 0.714\ldots$
$\qquad\quad \text{multiplier} = \sqrt{0.714\ldots} = 0.8451\ldots$
$(100 - x)\% = 84.51\ldots$
$\qquad\qquad x = 15.5$ to 1 decimal place
1 mark for finding value after 1 year; 1 mark for using formula with powers correct; 1 mark for finding multiplier; 1 mark for correct value of x to 1 decimal place. Total 4 marks.

Page 61, Compound measures

1. a Time = $\dfrac{9}{0.3} = 30\,s$
1 mark for writing or using time = $\dfrac{distance}{speed}$; 1 mark for correct answer.
b 54 km/h = 54 000 m/h = 900 m/min = 15 m/s
Distance in 10 s = 15 × 10 = 150 m
1 mark for converting speed to m/s (or you could convert speed to m/h and write 10 s as $\dfrac{1}{360}$ hour); 1 mark for using distance = speed × time; 1 mark for correct answer. Total 3 marks.

2. 400 000 cm² = 40 m²
Pressure = $\dfrac{24}{40} = 0.6\,N/m^2$
1 mark for correct answer circled.

Page 62, Direct & inverse proportion 1

1. a

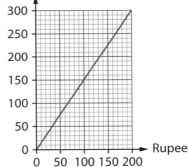

1 mark for line through origin and through point (100, 150); 1 mark for correct scale on both axes; 1 mark for both axes labelled. Total 3 marks.
Alternatively, you could have Yen on the x-axis and Rupee on the y-axis.

b Either use graph:

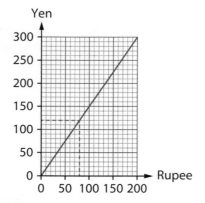

Or:

1 yen $= \frac{100}{150} = \frac{2}{3}$ rupees

So, 120 yen $= \frac{2}{3} \times 120 = 80$ rupees

1 mark for drawing lines on graph as shown; 1 mark for correct answer.

Alternatively, 1 mark for finding value of 1 yen (or another sensible number such as 10 yen or 20 yen); 1 mark for correct answer.

2. a Number of 'worker-hours' $= 12 \times 5 = 60$

Time $= 60 \div 15 = 4$ hours

1 mark for finding number of 'worker-hours'; 1 mark for correct answer.

b Number of gardeners $= 60 \div 2 = 30$

1 mark for dividing your number of 'worker-hours' from part a by 2; 1 mark for correct answer.

c

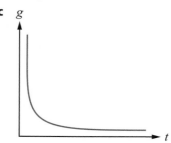

1 mark for correct shape, not crossing axes; 1 mark for completely correct, labelled graph (t and g can be the other way around).

Page 63, Direct & inverse proportion 2

1. $V = \frac{k}{P}$

$6 = \frac{k}{18}$

$\Rightarrow k = 108$

Equation is $V = \frac{108}{P} \left(\text{or } P = \frac{108}{V} \right)$

When $V = 4$,

$4 = \frac{108}{P}$

$P = \frac{108}{4} = 27$

1 mark for writing equation in correct form and substituting in values of V and P; 1 mark for using equation with value of k and substituting V = 4; 1 mark for correct answer. Total 3 marks.

2. $p = \frac{k_1}{r}$

$1 = \frac{k_1}{3} \Rightarrow k_1 = 3$

Equation is $p = \frac{3}{r}$

$r = k_2\sqrt{s}$

$3 = k_2\sqrt{36} \Rightarrow k_2 = \frac{1}{2}$

Equation is $r = \frac{1}{2}\sqrt{s}$

Substitute this into first equation:

$p = \dfrac{3}{\frac{1}{2}\sqrt{s}}$

$p = \frac{6}{\sqrt{s}}$

Alternatively, you could substitute first, then find the value of a single constant using fact that $p = 1$ when $s = 36$

1 mark for correct equations linking p and r and r and s; 1 mark for finding value of at least one constant; 1 mark for substituting to eliminate r; 1 mark for correct answer. Total 4 marks.

Page 64, Measures

1. a $39 \div 60^2 = 0.01083\ldots$ km/s

$0.01083 \times 1000 = 10.8$ m/s to 1 decimal place

1 mark for converting to either km/s or m/h (39 000); 1 mark for correct answer to 1 decimal place.

b Distance to meeting $= 11 \times 1.6 = 17.6$ km

Distance travelled in 25 minutes $= 39 \times \frac{25}{60} = 16.25$ km

$16.25 < 17.6$, so he will be late.

Or, time to travel to meeting $= \frac{17.6}{39} \times 60$
$= 27.1$ minutes

$27.1 > 25$, so he will be late.

1 mark for converting distance to km; 1 mark for distance travelled in 25 minutes (or time to travel 17.6 km); 1 mark for conclusion. Total 3 marks.

Alternatively:

Speed $= 39 \div 1.6 = 24.375$ mph

Distance travelled in 25 minutes $= 24.375 \times \frac{25}{60}$
$= 10.2$ miles

$10.2 < 11$, so he will be late.

Or, time to travel to meeting $= \frac{11}{24.375} \times 60$
$= 27.1$ minutes

$27.1 > 25$, so he will be late.

1 mark for converting speed to mph; 1 mark for finding distance travelled in 25 minutes (or time to travel 11 miles); 1 mark for conclusion. Total 3 marks.

2. a 2.2 litres $= 2200$ cm^3

$2200 \times 10^3 = 2200000$ mm^3

1 mark for converting to cm³; 1 mark for correct answer.

b $93000 \div 10^2 = 930$ cm^2

Total cost $= 930 \times 0.3$
$= £2.79$ (or 279p)

Or, cost $= 0.3 \div 10^2 = 0.003$ p/mm^2

Total cost $= 93000 \times 0.003 = £2.79$ (or 279p)

1 mark for converting surface area to cm² (or for converting price to p/mm²); 1 mark for correct answer.

Page 65, Angle rules

$3x = y + 85$ since corresponding angles are equal.

$y = x + 15$ since vertically opposite angles are equal.

Rearrange: $3x - y = 85$ **(1)**

            $x - y = -15$ **(2)**

(1) − **(2)**: $2x = 100$

            $x = 50°$

(2): $50 - y = -15$

          $y = 65°$

Or, use substitution: $3x = x + 15 + 85$

                     $2x = 100$ then as above

1 mark setting up equations, 1 mark for solving for one variable, 1 mark for substituting into other equation, 1 mark for both correct values. Total 4 marks.

Page 66, Triangles & quadrilaterals

1. $8x + 3x + 8x + x = 360$

               $20x = 360$

                  $x = 18°$

1 mark for correct answer circled.

2. $\angle ACB = \frac{1}{2}(180 - 50) = 65°$ since base angles of isosceles triangle are equal (and angles in triangle add up to 180°).

$\angle DCB = 180 - 65° = 115°$ since angles on straight line add up to 180°.

$y = 115°$ since corresponding angles are equal.

1 mark for angle at base of triangle; 1 mark for reason of angles in isosceles triangle; 1 mark for reason of angles on a straight line add up to 180°; 1 mark for correct answer with reason of corresponding angles are equal Total 4 marks.

Page 67, Polygons

1. $\frac{(n-2) \times 180}{n} = 156$

$180n - 360 = 156n$

        $24n = 360$

          $n = 15$

1 mark correct answer circled.

Alternatively:

Exterior angle $= 180 - 156 = 24$

$\frac{360}{n} = 24$

  $n = 15$

1 mark correct answer circled.

2. Exterior angle of regular pentagon $= 360 \div 5$

                           $= 72°$

Exterior angle of regular hexagon $= 360 \div 6$

                          $= 60°$

$x = 72 + 60 = 132°$

1 mark for finding exterior angle of regular pentagon and hexagon; 1 mark for adding; 1 mark for correct answer. Total 3 marks.

Alternatively:

Interior angle of regular pentagon $= \frac{(5-2) \times 180}{5}$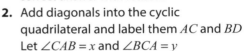

                    $= 108°$

Interior angle of regular hexagon $= \frac{(6-2) \times 180}{6}$

                    $= 120°$

$x = 360 - 120 - 108 = 132°$

1 mark for finding interior angle of regular pentagon and hexagon; 1 mark for subtracting from 360°; 1 mark for correct answer. Total 3 marks.

Page 68, Circle theorems 1

1. $y = 180 - 88 - 32 = 60°$ since angles in the same segment are equal.

1 mark for finding y; 1 mark for correct answer with reason.

2. Add diagonals into the cyclic quadrilateral and label them AC and BD

Let $\angle CAB = x$ and $\angle BCA = y$

Then $\angle BDA = y$ and $\angle BDC = x$ since angles in same segment are equal.

$\angle ABC = 180 - (x + y)$ since angles in triangle add up to 180°.

Therefore, $\angle ABC + \angle ADC = x + y + (180 - x - y)$

                                    $= 180°$ as required

1 mark for using theorem about angles in same segment to find two more angles; 1 mark for using angles in a triangle to find one of the angles of the cyclic quadrilateral; 1 mark for complete and clear proof with geometrical reasons. Total 3 marks.

Note that there are many possible proofs, and this is just one.

Page 69, Circle theorems 2

1. $\angle BCD = 38°$ by the alternate segment theorem.

$\angle OCD = 90°$ since angle between tangent and radius is 90°.

$x = 90 - 38 = 52°$

1 mark for correct use of alternate segment theorem;

1 mark for using $\angle OCD = 90°$; 1 mark for fully correct proof with all working and reasons given. Total 3 marks.

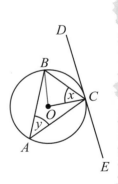

2. Add line BO

$\angle BOC = 2y$ since angle at the centre is 2 × angle at circumference.

$x = \frac{1}{2}(180 - 2y)$ since $\triangle OBC$ is isosceles.

$x = 90 - y$

$\angle OCD = 90°$ since angle between tangent and radius is 90°.

Therefore, $\angle BCD = 90 - (90 - y)$

                      $= y$

                      $= \angle BAC$ as required

1 mark for finding angle at centre; 1 mark for finding other angle in isosceles triangle; 1 mark for finding angle between tangent and chord; 1 mark for fully correct proof with all working and reasons given. Total 4 marks.

Page 70, Transformations

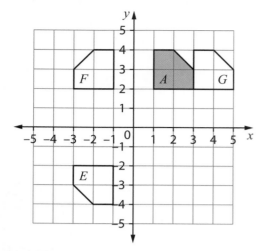

a Shape E shown above
1 mark for correct orientation; *1 mark* for fully correct drawing.

b Shape F shown above
1 mark for a reflection with at least one vertex in correct place; *1 mark* for fully correct drawing.

c Shape G shown above
1 mark for correct drawing.

Page 71, Enlargement

1. a

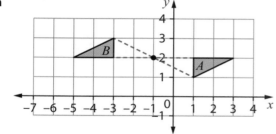

1 mark for correct size; *1 mark* for correct orientation; *1 mark* for fully correct drawing. Total 3 marks.

b Rotation of 180° about $(-1, 2)$
1 mark for rotation of 180°; *1 mark* for centre of rotation.

2.

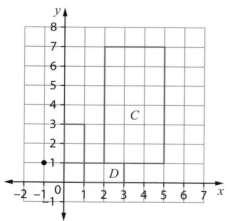

1 mark for correct dimensions of enlargement; *1 mark* for reflecting your enlargement in the line $y = x$ (even if your enlargement was wrong or in the wrong place); *1 mark* for fully correct answer. Total 3 marks.

Page 72, Congruent shapes

Both triangles are right-angled.
$AC = AB$
AD is common to both triangles.
Therefore, ABD and ACD are congruent using the RHS (right angle, hypotenuse, side) condition.
1 mark for $AC = AB$; *1 mark* for correct condition; *1 mark* for fully explained proof. Total 3 marks.

Page 73, Similar shapes

1. Scale factor $= \frac{6}{4} = 1.5$
Length of $VY = 6 \times 1.5 = 9\,\text{cm}$
Length of $WY = 9 - 6 = 3\,\text{cm}$
1 mark for finding scale factor; *1 mark* for finding length of VY; *1 mark* for correct answer. Total 3 marks.

2. $(SF)^3 = \frac{2.5}{20} = \frac{1}{8}$
$SF = \sqrt[3]{\frac{1}{8}} = \frac{1}{2}$
Length of shorter piece $\frac{1}{2} \times 60 = 30\,\text{cm}$
1 mark for finding what the mass has been multiplied by; *1 mark* for finding the cube root; *1 mark* for correct answer. Total 3 marks.

Page 74, Area and perimeter

a Area of rectangle $= 10 \times 30 = 300\,\text{m}^2$
Area of quarter circle $= \pi \times 10^2 \div 4 = 78.53\ldots\,\text{m}^2$
Total area $= 300 + 78.53\ldots = 379\,\text{m}^2$ (to the nearest integer)
1 mark for finding correct area of rectangle;
1 mark for using radius of 10 to find area of circle;
1 mark for dividing area of circle by 4 and adding to area of rectangle; *1 mark* for correct answer to the nearest integer. Total 4 marks.

b Circumference of circle $= 2 \times \pi \times 10 = 62.83\ldots\,\text{m}$
Perimeter $= 10 + 30 \times 2 + 10 + 62.83\ldots \div 4$
$= 96\,\text{m}$ (to nearest integer)
1 mark for finding circumference of circle and dividing by 4; *1 mark* for adding 5 correct lengths; *1 mark* for correct answer to the nearest integer. Total 3 marks.

Page 75, Plans and elevations

1. a

1 mark for correct plan. Note there are many possible solutions.

b

1 mark for correct elevation.

c

1 mark for correct elevation.

2. a

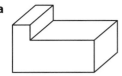

1 mark for a 3D solid with correct shape at front,
1 mark for fully correct prism.

b i 12 **ii** 18 **iii** 8

1 mark for each correct answer. Total 3 marks.

Page 76, Prisms and cylinders

1. Volume $= \frac{1}{2} \times x^2 \times 8 = 324$

$\qquad 4x^2 = 324$

$\qquad x^2 = 81$

$\qquad x = 9\,\text{cm}$

1 mark for using correct formula; 1 mark for correct method to solve for x; 1 mark for correct answer. Total 3 marks.

2. a Radius $= 6 \div 2 = 3\,\text{cm}$

Curved surface area $= 2 \times \pi \times 3 \times 20 = 120\pi$

Area of circular base $= \pi \times 3^2 = 9\pi$

Total surface area $= 120\pi + 9\pi = 129\pi\ (\text{cm}^2)$

1 mark for using correct formula for curved surface area; 1 mark for using correct formula for area of base; 1 mark for correct answer in terms of π. Total 3 marks.

b Volume $= 129\pi \times 0.2 = 25.8\pi$

Mass $=$ density $\times$ volume $= 0.6 \times 25.8\pi$

$\qquad = 15.48\pi = 48.63\ldots = 48.6\,\text{(g)}$ to 3 sf

1 mark for surface area $\times$ 0.2 (or allow $\times$ 2 for this mark); 1 mark for using mass $=$ density $\times$ volume; 1 mark for correct answer rounded to 3 sf. Total 3 marks.

Page 77, Spheres and pyramids

1. a Volume $= \frac{4}{3} \times \pi \times 12^3 = 7238.229\ldots$

$\qquad = 7240\ (\text{cm}^3)$ to 3 sf

1 mark for using correct formula for volume; 1 mark for correct answer rounded to 3 sf.

b Surface area $= 4 \times \pi \times 12^2 = 1809.557\ldots$

$\qquad = 1810\ (\text{cm}^2)$ to 3 sf

1 mark for using correct formula for surface area; 1 mark for correct answer rounded to 3 sf.

2. a Volume of sphere $= \frac{4}{3} \times \pi \times 2^3$

$\qquad = \frac{4}{3} \times \pi \times 8$

$\qquad = \frac{32}{3}\pi\ (\text{m}^3)$

Volume of hemisphere $= \frac{32}{3}\pi \div 2$

$\qquad = \frac{16}{3}\pi\ (\text{m}^3)$

1 mark for using formula for volume of sphere; 1 mark for dividing by 2; 1 mark for final answer in terms of π. Total 3 marks.

b Volume of hemisphere $= \frac{16}{3}\pi \times 100^3$

$\qquad = 16\,755\,161\ (\text{cm}^3)$

*1 mark for multiplying your answer from part **a** by 100^3 ($1\,000\,000$); 1 mark for correct answer.*

Page 78, Cones and frustums

1. a Volume $= \frac{1}{3} \times \pi \times 10^2 \times 24 = 800\pi\ (\text{cm}^3)$

1 mark for using correct formula (note that r is 10 as the diameter is 20); 1 mark for correct answer in terms of π

b Use Pythagoras' theorem to find slant height, l:

$l = \sqrt{24^2 + 10^2} = 26\,\text{cm}$

Curved surface area $= \pi \times 10 \times 26$

$\qquad = 260\pi\ (\text{cm}^2)$

1 mark for using Pythagoras' theorem to find slant height; 1 mark for using correct formula; 1 mark for correct answer in terms of π. Total 3 marks.

2. $\text{SF} = \frac{6}{30} = \frac{1}{5}$

Let height of the small cone be x cm.

$\frac{\text{Height of small cone}}{\text{Height of large cone}} = \frac{x}{20+x}$

$\text{SF} = \frac{1}{5} \Rightarrow \frac{x}{20+x} = \frac{1}{5}$

$5x = 20 + x$

$4x = 20$

$\ x = 5$

Height of small cone $= 5\,\text{cm}$

Height of large cone $= 25\,\text{cm}$

Volume of large cone $= \frac{1}{3} \times \pi \times 15^2 \times 25 = 1875\pi$

Volume of small cone $= \frac{1}{3} \times \pi \times 3^2 \times 5 = 15\pi$

Volume of frustum $= 1875\pi - 15\pi$

$\qquad = 1860\pi\ (\text{cm}^3)\ (\approx 5843\,\text{cm}^3)$

1 mark for finding scale factor; 1 mark for forming equation to find height of smaller cone; 1 mark for using formula for volume of cone; 1 mark for subtracting volumes; 1 mark for correct answer. Total 5 marks.

Page 79, Constructing triangles

1.

1 mark for 58° angle (to nearest 1°); 1 mark for two side lengths correct (to nearest mm); 1 mark for completely correct parallelogram. Total 3 marks.

2. a

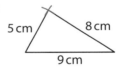

1 mark for 9 cm line and at least one correct arc; 1 mark for both arcs correct; 1 mark for completely correct triangle including construction lines. Total 3 marks.

b

1 mark for drawing arcs of equal radius from both ends of line; 1 mark for fully correct answer including construction lines.

Page 80, Perpendiculars and bisectors

1.

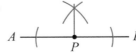

1 mark for attempting all the arcs; 1 mark for correct answer (to nearest degree) including all arcs. (You can use a protractor to check your line is perpendicular to AB)

2.

1 mark for attempting all the arcs; 1 mark for 70° angle drawn (to nearest degree) and all arcs drawn. (You can use a protractor to check the angle.)

Page 81, Loci

a Construct angle bisector:

1 mark for all arcs attempted; 1 mark for correct angle bisector. (You can use a protractor to check that each angle is 27°.)

b On your diagram for part **a**, draw circle of radius 3 cm with centre at A

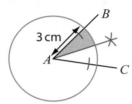

1 mark for drawing circle of radius 3 cm; 1 mark for shading above the angle bisector; 1 mark for shading inside the circle. Total 3 marks.

Page 82, Pythagoras' theorem

1. a $x = \sqrt{17^2 - 14^2} = 9.6$ cm

1 mark for using Pythagoras' theorem with 17 as the hypotenuse; 1 mark for correct answer to 1 decimal place.

b $y = \sqrt{4.2^2 + 7.6^2} = 8.7$ cm

1 mark for using Pythagoras' theorem with y as the hypotenuse; 1 mark for correct answer to 1 decimal place.

2. $12^2 + 5^2 = 144 + 25 = 169$; $13^2 = 169$ ✓

$2^2 + 3^2 = 4 + 9 = 13$; $4^2 = 16$, not 13 ✗

$8^2 + 6^2 = 64 + 36 = 100$; $10^2 = 100$ ✓

$7^2 + 24^2 = 49 + 576 = 625$; $25^2 = 625$ ✓

2 cm, 3 cm and 4 cm are not the side lengths of a right-angled triangle.

1 mark for correct answer circled.

Page 83, Trigonometry 1

1. $\cos 70° = \dfrac{0.5}{x}$

$x = \dfrac{0.5}{\cos 70°} = 1.46\ldots$

Length of plank = 1.46 m (to the nearest cm)

1 mark for using correct ratio with values in the correct places; 1 mark for correct answer to nearest cm.

2. Let the hypotenuse of the bottom triangle be y

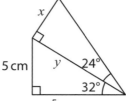

$\sin 32° = \dfrac{5}{y}$

$y = \dfrac{5}{\sin 32°} = 9.435\ldots$ cm

$\tan 24° = \dfrac{x}{9.435\ldots}$

$x = 9.435\ldots \times \tan 24° = 4.2$ cm

1 mark for using sin to attempt to find hypotenuse of bottom triangle; 1 mark for using tan to attempt to find x; 1 mark for correct answer to 1 decimal place. Total 3 marks.

Page 84, Trigonometry 2

1. For angle of elevation θ, $\tan \theta = \dfrac{80}{20}$

$\theta = \tan^{-1}\left(\dfrac{80}{20}\right) = 76°$ (to the nearest degree)

1 mark for using correct ratio with values in the correct places; 1 mark for correct answer to nearest degree.

2. $\sin \theta = \dfrac{x}{3x} = \dfrac{1}{3}$

$\theta = \sin^{-1}\left(\dfrac{1}{3}\right) = 19°$ (to nearest degree)

1 mark for using sin to attempt to find size of angle; 1 mark for correct answer to nearest degree.

Page 85, Bearings

1. a $220 - 180 = 40$

Bearing is 040°

1 mark for subtracting 180; 1 mark for correct answer written as a 3-digit bearing.

b

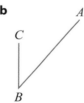

1 mark for lines drawn to scale, with AB = 20 cm and BC = 10 cm (this diagram is not to scale); 1 mark for CB vertical; 1 mark for angle CBA = 40°. Total 3 marks.

2. Sketch the situation. Let x and y be the unknown angles, as shown.

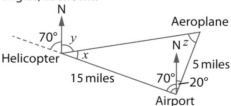

$\tan x = \dfrac{5}{15}$

$x = \tan^{-1}\left(\dfrac{5}{15}\right) = 18°$ (to nearest degree)

$y = 180 - 70 - 18 = 92°$

Bearing of aeroplane from helicopter = 092°

1 mark for sketch or for using fact there is a right-angled triangle; 1 mark for using tan to find an angle in triangle; 1 mark for subtracting 70° and your angle from 180°; 1 mark for correct answer. Total 4 marks.

Alternatively:
Consider the other unknown angle in the triangle. Let this be z
$\tan z = \frac{15}{5}$
$z = \tan^{-1}\left(\frac{15}{5}\right) = 72°$ (to nearest degree)
Bearing of airport from aeroplane = 20 + 180 = 200°
Bearing of helicopter from aeroplane = 200 + 72 = 272°
Bearing of aeroplane from helicopter = 272 − 180 = 092°
1 mark for sketch or for using fact there is a right-angled triangle; 1 mark for using tan to find an angle in triangle; 1 mark for adding your angle to the bearing of airport from aeroplane; 1 mark for correct answer. Total 4 marks.

Page 86, Exact values of sin, cos, tan

1. $\cos 30° = \frac{\sqrt{3}}{2} = \frac{x}{2}$
   $x = \sqrt{3}$ cm
   1 mark for correct answer circled.

2. $\tan x = \frac{1 + \sqrt{3}}{\left(\frac{\sqrt{3} + 3}{3}\right)} = \frac{3 + 3\sqrt{3}}{\sqrt{3} + 3} = \sqrt{3}$
   $x = 60°$
   1 mark for using correct ratio; 1 mark for simplifying ratio to $\sqrt{3}$; 1 mark for correct answer. Total 3 marks.

Page 87, Pythagoras' theorem in 3D

1. $4^2 + 4^2 + 4^2 = 3 \times 4^2$
   Length of longest diagonal $= \sqrt{3 \times 4^2}$
   $= 4\sqrt{3}$ cm
   1 mark for using formula for longest diagonal (or for finding length of hypotenuse of base); 1 mark for finding length of diagonal (could have $\sqrt{48}$); 1 mark for correct answer in simplest form. Total 3 marks.

2. $DB^2 = 8^2 + 8^2 = 128$
   $DB = \sqrt{128} = 8\sqrt{2}$
   Let M be midpoint of square $BCDE$
   Then $MB = \frac{1}{2}DB = \frac{1}{2} \times 8\sqrt{2}$
   Consider triangle ABM:
   $AM^2 = 14^2 - \left(\frac{1}{2} \times 8\sqrt{2}\right)^2$
   $= 164$
   $AM =$ height of pyramid $= \sqrt{164}$
   $= 12.8$ cm (1 decimal place)
   1 mark for finding length of hypotenuse of base; 1 mark for using half of this hypotenuse and attempting to find height of pyramid; 1 mark for correct answer. Total 3 marks.

Page 88, Trigonometry in 3D

1. Find length of HF. Using Pythagoras in triangle FGH,
   $HF^2 = 14^2 + 4^2 = 212$
   $HF = \sqrt{212} = 14.56\ldots$ cm
   Consider triangle HFB
   $\angle BHF = \tan^{-1}\left(\frac{8}{14.56\ldots}\right) = 28.8°$
   Alternatively, find length of HB:
   $HB^2 = 14^2 + 4^2 + 8^2 = 276$
   $HB = 16.61\ldots$ cm
   Then use sin to find angle:
   $\angle BHF = \sin^{-1}\left(\frac{8}{16.61\ldots}\right) = 28.8°$
   1 mark for using Pythagoras' theorem to find HF (or HB); 1 mark for correct length HF (or HB); 1 mark for using tan (or sin) to find angle; 1 mark for correct answer. Total 4 marks.

2. Let M be the midpoint of EF. Consider the triangle DMB
   Using Pythagoras in triangle DME,
   $DM^2 = 7^2 - 3^2 = 40$
   $DM = \sqrt{40} = 6.32\ldots$ cm
   Using Pythagoras in triangle DEB,
   $DB^2 = 12^2 + 7^2 = 193$
   $DB = \sqrt{193} = 13.89\ldots$ cm
   In triangle DMB, the angle you want is
   $\angle DBM = \sin^{-1}\left(\frac{6.32\ldots}{13.89\ldots}\right) = 27.1°$
   1 mark for using Pythagoras' theorem to find any length in the triangle DMB; 1 mark for finding a correct length in triangle DMB; 1 mark for finding a second correct length in triangle DMB (could have BM = 11.6 cm); 1 mark for using either sin, cos or tan to find angle DBM; 1 mark for correct answer. Total 5 marks.

Page 89, sine and cosine rules

a $\cos x = \frac{29^2 + 32^2 - 27^2}{2 \times 29 \times 32}$
   $= \frac{71}{116}$ or 0.612…
   $x = \cos^{-1}\left(\frac{71}{116}\right) = 52.3°$ (1 decimal place)
   1 mark for using cosine rule; 1 mark for correct value of cos x; 1 mark for correct answer. Total 3 marks.

b Find third angle in triangle: 180 − 58 − 81 = 41°
   $\frac{x}{\sin 41°} = \frac{17}{\sin 58°}$
   $x = \frac{17 \sin 41°}{\sin 58°} = 13.2$ cm (1 decimal place)
   1 mark for finding third angle; 1 mark for correct use of sine rule; 1 mark for rearranging correctly to make x the subject; 1 mark for correct answer. Total 3 marks.

Page 90, Area of a triangle

1. Area $= \frac{1}{2} \times 31.6 \times 43.8 \times \sin 98°$
   $= 685.3$ cm^2 (1 decimal place)
   1 mark for using formula with correct values; 1 mark for correct answer.

2. Use cosine rule to find one of the angles, e.g.

$$\cos\theta = \frac{18^2 + 17^2 - 15^2}{2 \times 18 \times 17} = \frac{97}{153} \text{ or } 0.6339\ldots$$

$$\theta = \cos^{-1}\left(\frac{97}{153}\right) = 50.65\ldots°$$

$$\text{Area} = \frac{1}{2} \times 18 \times 17 \times \sin(50.65\ldots°)$$

$$= 118.3 \text{ cm}^2 \text{ (1 decimal place)}$$

1 mark for using cosine rule to find one of the angles;
1 mark for correct value of angle (other two are 61.2° and 68.1°); 1 mark for using area formula with correct values;
1 mark for correct answer. Total 4 marks.

Page 91, Sectors, arcs & segments

1. a Area $= \frac{35}{360} \times \pi \times 9^2 = 24.7 \text{ cm}^2$
1 mark for using correct formula; 1 mark for answer correct to 1 decimal place.

b Arc length $= \frac{35}{360} \times 2 \times \pi \times 9 = 5.5 \text{ cm}$
1 mark for using correct formula; 1 mark for answer correct to 1 decimal place.

c Perimeter $= 5.49\ldots + 2 \times 9 = 23.5 \text{ cm}$
1 mark for adding 2×9 to the value from part b for arc length; 1 mark for answer correct to 1 decimal place.

2. Area of sector $= \frac{160}{360} \times \pi \times 7^2 = 68.4\ldots \text{ cm}^2$

Area of triangle $= \frac{1}{2} = \times 7^2 \times \sin 160° = 8.37\ldots \text{ cm}^2$

Area of segment $= 68.4\ldots - 8.37\ldots$

$$= 60.0 \text{ cm}^2 \text{ (1 decimal place)}$$

1 mark for area of sector; 1 mark for area of triangle;
1 mark for subtracting to get area of segment; 1 mark for correct answer. Total 4 marks.

Page 92, Vectors 1

$$\overrightarrow{AC} = \overrightarrow{AD} + \overrightarrow{DC}$$

$$= \overrightarrow{AD} - \overrightarrow{CD}$$

$$= \begin{pmatrix} 3 \\ -1 \end{pmatrix} - \begin{pmatrix} -2 \\ -5 \end{pmatrix} = \begin{pmatrix} 5 \\ 4 \end{pmatrix}$$

1 mark for correct answer circled.

Page 93, Vectors 2

a $\overrightarrow{NM} = \overrightarrow{NA} + \overrightarrow{AM}$

$$= \frac{1}{6}\overrightarrow{OA} + \frac{1}{2}\overrightarrow{AB}$$

$$= \frac{1}{6}\mathbf{a} + \frac{1}{2}(-\mathbf{a} + \mathbf{b})$$

$$= -\frac{1}{3}\mathbf{a} + \frac{1}{2}\mathbf{b}$$

1 mark for using $\overrightarrow{NA} = \frac{1}{6}\overrightarrow{OA}$ (or $\overrightarrow{NO} = \frac{5}{6}\overrightarrow{AO}$); 1 mark for using $\overrightarrow{AM} = \frac{1}{2}\overrightarrow{AB}$ (or $\overrightarrow{BM} = \frac{1}{2}\overrightarrow{BA}$); 1 mark for correct working leading to the correct answer. Total 3 marks.

b If NMC is a straight line, then $\overrightarrow{NC}$ must be a multiple of $\overrightarrow{NM}$

$$\overrightarrow{NC} = \frac{5}{6}\overrightarrow{AO} + \overrightarrow{AO}$$

$$= -\frac{5}{6}\mathbf{a} + k\mathbf{b}$$

Compare this to $\overrightarrow{NM} = -\frac{1}{3}\mathbf{a} + \frac{1}{2}\mathbf{b}$:

$$\overrightarrow{NM} = \frac{2}{5}\overrightarrow{NC} \text{ since } \frac{2}{5} \times \left(-\frac{5}{6}\mathbf{a}\right) = -\frac{1}{3}a$$

Then $\frac{1}{2}\mathbf{b} = \frac{2}{5}k\mathbf{b}$

$$k = \frac{5}{4}$$

1 mark for correct vector expression for $\overrightarrow{NC}$; 1 mark for comparing to $\overrightarrow{NM}$; 1 mark for correct answer. Total 3 marks.

Page 94, Sampling

a The data is secondary since Aston didn't collect it himself.
1 mark for correct answer including explanation.

b $\frac{5}{20} = \frac{1}{4}$ of the days in the sample had light rain.
Estimated number of days with light rain in the whole summer holiday $= \frac{1}{4}$ of $48 = 12$
1 mark for finding the proportion of days with light rain in the sample; 1 mark for correct answer.

c Aston could take sample data from different years.
1 mark for correct explanation.

Page 95, Averages and spread

1. a The total frequency is 20, so need the average of the 10th and 11th numbers of items, which are 5 and 6
Median $= \frac{5 + 6}{2} = 5.5$ items
1 mark for considering average of 10th and 11th values;
1 mark for correct answer.

b Mode = 6 items (highest frequency)
1 mark for correct answer.

c

No. of items	3	4	5	6	7	8	Total
Frequency	1	5	4	7	2	1	20
No. of items × frequency	3	20	20	42	14	8	107

Mean $= 107 \div 20 = 5.35$ items
1 mark for multiplying each value by its frequency;
1 mark for dividing total of these values by total frequency; 1 mark for correct answer. Total 3 marks.

d Range $= 8 - 3 = 5$
1 mark for correct answer.

2.

Items of homework	0	1	2	3	4	Total
Frequency	2	5	4	1	2	14
Items of homework × frequency	0	5	8	3	8	24

Mean $= 24 \div 14 = 1.7$ (1 dp)
1 mark for multiplying each value by its frequency;
1 mark for dividing total of these values by total frequency; 1 mark for correct answer. Total 3 marks.

Page 96, Grouped data

a Modal class is $0 \leqslant t < 20$
1 mark for correct answer.

b

Time (t mins)	Frequency	Running total
$0 \leqslant t < 20$	35	35
$20 \leqslant t < 40$	20	55
$40 \leqslant t < 60$	16	71
$60 \leqslant t < 80$	9	80

There are 80 in total so median is around the 40th which is in the $20 \leqslant t < 40$ class.
1 mark for doing a running total or attempting to find the 40th or 41st value; 1 mark for correct answer.

c

Time (t mins)	Mid-point	Frequency	Midpoint × frequency
$0 \leqslant t < 20$	10	35	350
$20 \leqslant t < 40$	30	20	600
$40 \leqslant t < 60$	50	16	800
$60 \leqslant t < 80$	70	9	630
Total		80	2380

Estimate for mean = 2380 ÷ 80 = 29.75 mins
1 mark for correct midpoints; 1 mark for multiplying midpoints by frequencies and adding up; 1 mark for correct answer. Total 3 marks.

Page 97, Interquartile range

a Mean = $\frac{316}{15}$ = 21.1 minutes
1 mark for attempting to add up values and divide by 15; 1 mark for correct answer.

b $\frac{1}{2}(15 + 1) = 8$
Median = 8th value = 17 minutes
1 mark for correct answer.

c $\frac{1}{4}(15 + 1) = 4$
Lower quartile = 4th value = 12
$\frac{3}{4}(15 + 1) = 12$
Lower quartile = 12th value = 27
Interquartile range = 27 − 12 = 15 minutes
1 mark for finding correct lower or upper quartile; 1 mark for subtracting your lower quartile from your upper quartile; 1 mark for correct answer. Total 3 marks.

Page 98, Simple charts

1. a Total ice creams bought for children = 70
Proportion that were vanilla = $\frac{14}{70} = \frac{1}{5}$
Angle for vanilla = $\frac{1}{5} \times 360 = 72°$
1 mark for finding proportion that were vanilla; 1 mark for correct answer.

b The proportion of ice creams bought for adults that were vanilla is bigger since fewer ice creams were bought for adults. Therefore, the angle of the sector will be bigger (120°).
1 mark for referring to proportion (or fewer ice creams in total); 1 mark for complete explanation.

2.

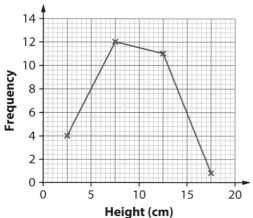

1 mark for plotting at least two correct points; 1 mark for 4 points (at least two correct) joined with straight lines; 1 mark for completely correct graph including labels on axes. Total 3 marks.

Page 99, Scatter graphs

1. It's an outlier and probably a mistake as it is very unlikely a 5 year old will be able to text this fast.
1 mark for correct answer.

2. a The points do not lie close to a straight line.
b No linear correlation but possible non-linear relationship.
1 mark for each correct answer.

Page 100, Lines of best fit

a Negative correlation (between temperature and cost)
1 mark for correct answer.

b

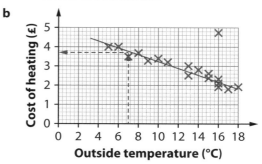

Approximately £3.70 (per day)
1 mark for drawing line of best fit, ignoring the outlier; 1 mark for sensible estimate from your line of best fit, including units (between £3.50 and £4.00).

c Gradient ≈ 0.2
A 1°C decrease in outside temperature leads to an increase in the cost of heating of £0.20 per day.
1 mark for estimating gradient; 1 mark for correct answer from your estimate including units (accept anything between £0.17 and £0.23).

d You don't have data for when the temperature is lower than 5 °C so this would be extrapolation and hence unreliable.
1 mark for correct explanation.

Page 101, Time series

a The general trend of the cost of strawberries is increasing.
1 mark for correct answer.

b They are cheapest in summer.
1 mark for correct answer.

c Mean = $\frac{3 + 2.5 + 3}{3}$ = £2.83
1 mark for using correct 3 values from graph; 1 mark for correct answer.

Page 102, Box plots

a Median = 10th value = 5
Lower quartile = 5th value = 4
Upper quartile = 15th value = 6

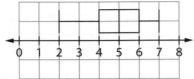

Number of pieces of homework

1 mark for correct values of quartiles written down or shown on box plot; 1 mark for box between your upper and lower quartiles; 1 mark for median drawn on at 5; 1 mark for completely correct answer including a scale. Total 4 marks.

b 25% of year 7 students have at least **4** pieces of homework.
1 mark for correct answer.

c The median for GCSE students (5) is higher than for year 7 students (3), so GCSE students have more homework on average.
The interquartile range for GCSE students (2) is smaller than for year 7 students (3), so the number of pieces of homework is more consistent across GCSE students than year 7 students.
1 mark for comparing medians; 1 mark for comparing interquartile range (or range). (1 mark only if you compare the smallest/largest values.)

Page 103, Cumulative frequency

a

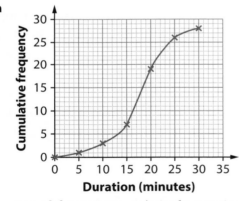

1 mark for correct cumulative frequencies (1, 3, 7, 19, 26, 28); 1 mark for plotting against end points of classes; 1 mark for correct points, joined with a smooth curve. Total 3 marks.

b **i** Median ≈ 18 minutes
1 mark for correct answer.

ii Lower quartile ≈ 15 minutes
Upper quartile ≈ 21 minutes
Interquartile range ≈ 21 – 15 = 6 minutes
1 mark for finding correct lower or upper quartile by drawing line across and subtracting your lower quartile from your upper quartile; 1 mark for correct answer.

c Upper bound = 30 – 0 = 30 minutes
Lower bound = 25 – 5 = 20 minutes
1 mark for correct upper bound; 1 mark for correct lower bound.

Page 104, Histograms

1. For the first bar,
frequency density = $\frac{5}{50}$ = 0.1
You can complete the vertical scale:

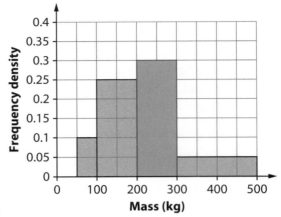

Mass (m kg)	Frequency
$50 \leq m < 100$	5
$100 \leq m < 200$	**0.25 × 100 = 25**
$200 \leq m < 300$	30
$300 \leq m < 500$	**0.05 × 200 = 10**

Complete the third bar for $200 \leq m < 300$:
Frequency density = 30 ÷ 100 = 0.3
1 mark for correct scale on histogram; 1 mark for each correct value in table; 1 mark for correct bar drawn. Total 4 marks.

2. a Mean ≈ $\frac{3 \times 3 + 8 \times 10 + 11 \times 7 + 13 \times 6 + 16 \times 6}{3 + 10 + 7 + 6 + 6}$
= $\frac{340}{32}$ = 10.625 s
1 mark for using correct midpoints (3, 8, 11, 13, 16); 1 mark for using correct frequencies (3, 10, 7, 6, 6); 1 mark for attempting to use correct formula for mean; 1 mark for correct answer. Total 4 marks.

b Assumed that the times are equally spaced within each class.
1 mark for correct answer.

Page 105, Theoretical probability

1. a $0.4 + x + 2x = 1$
$3x = 0.6$
$x = 0.2$
1 mark for forming correct equation; 1 mark for attempting to solve the equation; 1 mark for correct value of x. Total 3 marks.

b P(yellow) = 2 × 0.2 = 0.4
1 mark for correct answer.

2. a Probability of losing = $1 - \left(\frac{1}{5} + \frac{1}{3}\right)$
= $1 - \frac{8}{15}$
= $\frac{7}{15}$
1 mark for subtracting from 1 with correct method for adding both fractions or subtracting one of the fractions from 1; 1 mark for correct answer.

b Probability of not winning $= 1 - \dfrac{2}{x}$

$= \dfrac{x-2}{x}$

1 mark for subtracting from 1; 1 mark for correct answer.

Page 106, Outcomes and possibility spaces

1. Number of codes $= 5 \times 5 \times 8 = 200$
1 mark for correct answer circled.

2. The second and third times there are 6 and 5 to choose from respectively, so possible combinations $= 7 \times 6 \times 5 = 210$
1 mark for $7 \times 6 \times 5$; 1 mark for correct answer.

Page 107, Probability experiments

1. a

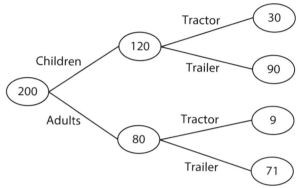

1 mark for a frequency tree with at least one correct set of branches; 1 mark for correct frequency tree with fewer than three labels or frequencies incorrect or missing; 1 mark for completely correct frequency tree. Total 3 marks.

b Probability $= \dfrac{71+90}{200} = \dfrac{161}{200} = 0.805$
1 mark for adding to find total number who had trailer ride; 1 mark for correct answer as a fraction or a decimal.

2. Let x be number she selected.

$\dfrac{x-5}{x} = 0.8$

$x - 5 = 0.8x$

$0.2x = 5$

$x = 25$

1 mark for forming correct equation; 1 mark for attempt to solve; 1 mark for correct answer. Total 3 marks. Alternatively, you could solve $\dfrac{5}{x} = 0.2$

Page 108, Expected results

1. a You would expect 3 heads not 1, but this is a very small number of trials so the results don't suggest the coin is biased.
1 mark for correct answer including reason.

b You would expect approximately 50 heads not 25, so this does suggest that the coin is biased.
1 mark for correct answer including reason.

2. Expected number of positive results $= 20 \times 2x = 6$
Therefore, $x = 0.15$
P(negative) $= 1 - 5x$

$= 1 - 0.25$

$= 0.75$

Expected number of negative results $= 40 \times 0.75 = 30$
1 mark for equation for expected number of possible results; 1 mark for solving for x; 1 mark for attempt at finding probability of negative result; 1 mark for correct final answer. Total 4 marks.

Page 109, Tree diagrams

1. a

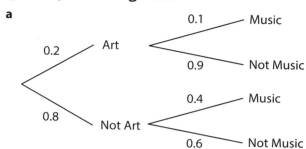

1 mark for tree diagram with 0.2 and 0.8 correct; 1 mark for 0.1 and 0.4 correct; 1 mark for completely correct tree diagram. Total 3 marks.

b i P(doesn't study Art or Music) $= 0.8 \times 0.6 = 0.48$
1 mark for multiplying along branches; 1 mark for correct answer.

ii P(Music) $= 0.2 \times 0.1 + 0.8 \times 0.4 = 0.02 + 0.32$

$= 0.34$

1 mark for adding two probabilities found by multiplying along branches; 1 mark for correct answer.

2.

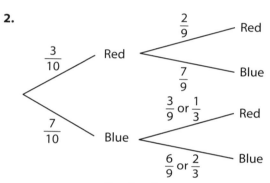

P(both blue) $= \dfrac{7}{10} \times \dfrac{2}{3} = \dfrac{7}{15}$

P(at least one red) $= 1 - \dfrac{7}{15} = \dfrac{8}{15}$

1 mark for tree diagram with $\dfrac{3}{10}$ and $\dfrac{7}{10}$ correct; 1 mark for any two probabilities correct on second set of branches; 1 mark for completely correct tree diagram; 1 mark for using 1 – P(both blue) or for using P(one red) + P(both red); 1 mark for correct answer. Total 5 marks.

Page 110, Conditional probability 1

a P(tea given milk) $= \dfrac{12}{30}\left(= \dfrac{2}{5}\right)$
1 mark for correct answer circled.

b P(milk given tea) $= \dfrac{12}{15} = \dfrac{4}{5}$
P(milk given coffee) $= \dfrac{18}{30} = \dfrac{3}{5}$
$\dfrac{4}{5} > \dfrac{3}{5}$
Amy is correct (people are more likely to have milk in tea than in coffee).
1 mark for calculating P(milk given tea); 1 mark for calculating P(milk given coffee); 1 mark for correct conclusion with explanation. Total 3 marks.

Page 111, Conditional probability 2

Represent the situation using a tree diagram, with
S = strawberry and R = raspberry:

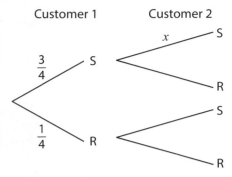

Customer 1   Customer 2

a $\frac{11}{20} = P(S \text{ and } S) = \frac{3}{4} \times x$

$x = \frac{11}{20} \div \frac{3}{4} = \frac{11}{15}$

Let there be r jars of raspberry.

Then $x = \frac{3r-1}{4r-1}$

$\frac{3r-1}{4r-1} = \frac{11}{15}$

$r = 4$

There are 4 jars of raspberry jam and in total 16 jars
of jam.

*1 mark for using multiplication of probabilities; 1 mark
for $\frac{11}{20} \div \frac{3}{4}$; 1 mark for correct answer. Total 3 marks.*

b Complete the tree diagram:

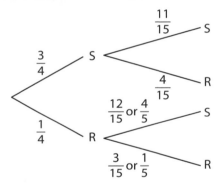

P(both chose same) = P(S and S) + P(R and R)

$= \frac{11}{20} + \frac{1}{4} \times \frac{1}{5}$

$= \frac{12}{20}$ or $\frac{3}{5}$

P(both chose strawberry given both chose the
same)

$= \frac{P(\text{both chose strawberry})}{P(\text{both chose same})}$

$= \frac{\frac{11}{20}}{\frac{3}{5}} = \frac{11}{12}$

*1 mark for probability of both choosing the same;
1 mark for attempting to use conditional probability rule;
1 mark for correct answer. Total 3 marks.*

Page 112, Set notation

1. a The numbers in set $A \cup B$ are 1, 2, 3, 5, 7, 9
*1 mark for all the correct numbers and no incorrect
numbers.*

b The numbers in set B' are 1, 4, 6, 8, 9, 10
*1 mark for all the correct numbers and no incorrect
numbers.*

2.

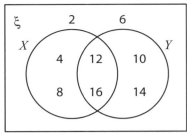

*1 mark for Venn diagram with rectangle and two
overlapping circles (or ovals); 1 mark for only 12 and 16
in the intersection; 1 mark for only 2 and 6 outside both
circles in the universal set; 1 mark for fully correct Venn
diagram. Total 4 marks.*

Page 113, Probability from Venn diagrams

1. a $P(A) = \frac{3}{9}\left(\text{or } \frac{1}{3}\right)$ **b** $P(B) = \frac{4}{9}$

c $P(A \cap B) = \frac{1}{9}$ **d** $P(A \cup B) = \frac{6}{9}\left(\text{or } \frac{2}{3}\right)$

e $P(A') = \frac{6}{9}\left(\text{or } \frac{2}{3}\right)$

1 mark for each correct answer. Total 5 marks.

2. P(netball given badminton) $= \frac{5+3}{5+3+7+2} = \frac{8}{17}$
*1 mark for restricting sample space to badminton (or for
using conditional probability rule); 1 mark for correct
answer.*

Pages 116–117, Calculating with bounds

Check-up box

1. 30 minutes = 0.5 hours
Average speed $= \frac{18}{0.5} = 36$ mph

2. Bus arrives at bus stop at 08:48
Bus journey is from 08:48 to 09:22 which is
12 + 22 = 34 minutes

3. $3.35 \leq n < 3.45$

4. $21.5 \leq t < 22.5$

Exam corner

1. Need (upper bound Adam) – (lower bound Lee)
Upper bound Adam: 167.5 cm
Lower bound Lee: 145.5 cm
Maximum difference = 167.5 – 145.5 = 22 cm
*1 mark for bounds calculated; 1 mark for correct
calculation; 1 mark for correct answer. Total 3 marks.*

2. a Circumference $= 2\pi r$
Lower bound for r is 5.55 cm
Minimum circumference $= \pi \times 5.55 \times 2 = 34.87\ldots$
$= 34.87$ cm (to 4 sf)
*1 mark for correct lower bound; 1 mark for correct
final answer.*

b Area $= \pi r^2$
Upper bound for r is 5.65 cm
Maximum area $= \pi \times 5.65^2 = 100.28\ldots$
$= 100.3$ cm^2 (to 4 sf)
*1 mark for correct upper bound; 1 mark for correct
final answer.*

3. Upper bound distance = 295 miles
Lower bound distance = 285 miles
Upper bound speed = 62.5 mph
Lower bound speed = 57.5 mph
Upper bound for time = $\dfrac{\text{upper distance}}{\text{lower speed}} = \dfrac{295}{57.5} = 5.13...$ hours

Lower bound for time = $\dfrac{\text{lower distance}}{\text{upper speed}} = \dfrac{285}{62.5} = 4.56$ hours

Estimate for the journey time is 5 hours because both times round to 5 to the nearest whole number.
1 mark for any two correct bounds for distance or speed; 1 mark for correct calculation of upper or lower bound for time; 1 mark for 5 hours; 1 mark for correct explanation. Total 4 marks.

4. Upper bound for $AC = \dfrac{23.5}{\frac{1}{2} \times 8.15 \sin 31.5°} = 11.0$ cm

Upper bound for $AC = \dfrac{22.5}{\frac{1}{2} \times 8.25 \sin 32.5°} = 10.2$ cm

1 mark for using correct formula; 1 mark for correct upper bound; 1 mark for correct lower bound. Total 3 marks.

Pages 118–119, Forming & solving equations

Check-up box

1. $y = \dfrac{5 - 6x}{2}$

2. $4x^2 - 4x + 1$

3. $(x - 2)(x + 7)$

4. $(x - 3)(x - 4) = 0$, $x = 3$ or $x = 4$

5. $2x + y = 8 (1)$, $x - y = 1 (2)$
$(1) + (2): 3x = 9$, $x = 3$, $y = 2$

Exam corner

1. Let m = Max's age and s = Sam's age.
$m - s = 5$
$m + 3 = 3s \Rightarrow m - 3s = -3$
Subtract: $2s = 8$, $s = 4$
Substitute into first equation:
$m - 4 = 5$, $m = 9$
Sam is 4 years old and Max is 9 years old.
1 mark for forming each initial equation; 1 mark for subtracting the equations to eliminate m; 1 mark for each correct answer. Total 4 marks.

2. Let x = number of 10p coins and y = number of 5p coins.
$x + y = 12 \Rightarrow 5x + 5y = 60$ (multiplying by 5)
$10x + 5y = 80$
Subtract: $5x = 20$, $x = 4$
Substitute into first equation:
$4 + y = 12$, $y = 8$
He has four 10p coins and eight 5p coins.
1 mark for scaling one equation to make coefficients of x or y the same; 1 mark for subtracting the equations to eliminate x or y; 1 mark for each correct answer. Total 4 marks.

3. Write the equations equal to each other.
$2x - 1 = x^2 + x - 21$ (or use substitution)
Rearrange to give $x^2 - x - 20 = 0$
Factorise: $(x - 5)(x + 4) = 0$
$x = 5$ or $x = -4$
When $x = 5$, $y = (2 \times 5) - 1 = 9$
When $x = -4$, $y = (2 \times -4) - 1 = -9$
1 mark for either substitution or making the equations equal; 1 mark for solving quadratic; 1 mark each for correct values of x and y. Total 4 marks.

4. Form the equations: $a^2 + b^2 = 8$, $a - b = 4$
Rearrange linear equation to give $a = 4 + b$
Substitute into quadratic:
$(4 + b)^2 + b^2 = 8$
Expand and simplify:
$b^2 + 4b + 4 = 0$
$(b + 2)^2 = 0$
$b = -2$
$a - (-2) = 4$, $a = 2$
1 mark for each equation formed; 1 mark for correct expansion; 1 mark each for correct values of a and b (values for a and b could be switched). Total 5 marks.

5. $x^2 + (2x + 1)^2 = 2$
$5x^2 + 4x - 1 = 0$
$(5x - 1)(x + 1) = 0$
$x = \dfrac{1}{5}, -1$
When $x = \dfrac{1}{5}$, $y = 2\left(\dfrac{1}{5}\right) + 1 = \dfrac{7}{5}$
When $x = -1$, $y = 2(-1) + 1 = -1$
$A(-1, -1)$, $B\left(\dfrac{1}{5}, \dfrac{7}{5}\right)$
$AB = \sqrt{\left(\dfrac{6}{5}\right)^2 + \left(\dfrac{12}{5}\right)^2}$
$= \dfrac{6\sqrt{5}}{5}$ (= 2.68 to 3 sf)
1 mark for substituting for y (or x) into quadratic; 1 mark for method to solve quadratic; 1 mark for correct values of x (or y); 1 mark for correct values for both variables; 1 mark for method to find length; 1 mark for correct length. Total 6 marks.

Pages 120–121, Forming algebraic proof

Check-up box

1. $-2n - 10$

2. $2n + 9$

3. $5x + 7 - 2x + 10 = 3x + 17$

4. $n^2 + 4 - n^2 - 4n - 4 = -4n$

Exam corner

1. a Using Pythagoras' theorem:
$(x + 1)^2 + x^2 = (x + 2)^2$
Expand and simplify LHS: $x^2 + 2x + 1 + x^2 = 2x^2 + 2x + 1$
Expand and simplify RHS: $x^2 + 4x + 4$
Write the two expressions as identical and rearrange: $2x^2 + 2x + 1 \equiv x^2 + 4x + 4$
$x^2 - 2x - 3 \equiv 0$ as required
1 mark for using Pythagoras to form equation; 1 mark for expanding correctly; 1 mark for rearranging. Total 3 marks.

b Factorising $x^2 - 2x - 3 = 0$

$(x - 3)(x + 1) = 0$

$x = 3$ or $x = -1$

Ignore $x = -1$ because you can't have a negative length. Sides are 3 cm, 5 cm and 4 cm.

1 mark for correct factorising; 1 mark for ignoring $x = -1$; 1 mark for 3 correct side lengths. Total 3 marks.

2. $(4n + 1)^2 \equiv 16n^2 + 8n + 1$

$(4n - 1)^2 \equiv 16n^2 - 8n + 1$

$(4n + 1)^2 - (4n - 1)^2 \equiv (16n^2 + 8n + 1) - (16n^2 - 8n + 1)$

$\equiv 16n$

This is a multiple of 16 for positive integer values of n.

1 mark for correct expansion; 1 mark for $16n$; 1 mark for explanation. Total 3 marks.

3. Let two consecutive integers be n and $n + 1$

Difference between the squares is $(n + 1)^2 - n^2$

Expand and simplify:

$(n + 1)^2 - n^2 \equiv n^2 + 2n + 1 - n^2 \equiv 2n + 1$

$2n + 1 \equiv n + (n + 1)$, hence proven.

1 mark for representing two consecutive integers; 1 mark for correct expression for difference of squares; 1 mark for $2n + 1$ seen; 1 mark for explanation. Total 4 marks.

4. Sequence has nth term $4n - 1$

Difference of squares of any two terms

$= (4n - 2)^2 - (4m - 2)^2$ where n, m integers

$= (16n^2 - 16n + 4) - (16m^2 - 16m + 4)$

$= 16(n^2 - m^2) - 16(n - m)$

$= 16(n - m)(n + m) - 16(n - m)$

$= 16(n - m)[n + m - 1]$

If $n - m$ is even, then expression is a multiple of 32

If $n - m$ is odd, then $n + m$ is odd, so $n + m - 1$ is even, so expression is a multiple of 32

1 mark for nth term of sequence; 1 mark for forming difference of squares; 1 mark for writing with 16 as common factor; 1 mark for reasoning and conclusion. Total 4 marks.

Pages 122–123, Tricky ratio questions

Check-up box

1. 36 counters = 3 parts, so each part = 12 counters. There are $2 \times 12 = 24$ red counters.

2. $3 : 1$

3. 5 parts = £30, so 1 part is £6. Ruby gets $6 \times 3 = £18$

Exam corner

1.

Florence gets £300 and this is 3 parts, so James gets £100

This £400 given to James and Florence is $\frac{1}{3}$ of the amount remaining after buying the bike.

$\frac{2}{3} = £800$ is put into savings account.

This £400 + £800 = £1200 is 75% of the amount inherited.

Total inherited is £1600

1 mark for £400 given to cousins; 1 mark for £800 into savings account; 1 mark for £1200 as 75% of total; 1 mark for correct answer. Total 4 marks.

2. Comparing ratios involving sheep, LCM is 6

Chickens : sheep : pigs = 21 : 6 : 2

116 animals in total, so each part = $116 \div 29 = 4$

Number of pigs = 8

1 mark for comparing ratios involving sheep; 1 mark for correct overall ratio; 1 mark for $116 \div 29$; 1 mark for correct final answer. Total 4 marks.

3. Let x be number of sticks and y be number of balls.

$x : y = 3 : 2 \Rightarrow y = \frac{2}{3}x$

$(x - 2) : (y - 3) = 8 : 5 \Rightarrow y - 3 = \frac{5}{8}(x - 2)$

$\frac{2}{3}x - 3 = \frac{5}{8}(x - 2)$

$\frac{1}{24}x = \frac{7}{4}$

$x = 42, y = 28$

42 sticks and 28 balls

1 mark for forming equations; 1 mark for method to solve; 1 mark for correct values of x or y; 1 mark for both values correct and given in context. Total 4 marks.

Pages 124–125, Scale factor & similarity

Check-up box

1. $3 \times 10^2 = 300 \, \text{mm}^2$

2. $3000 \div 100^3 = 0.003 \, \text{m}^3$

3. $\sqrt{25} = 5 \, \text{cm}$

$5 \times 10 = 50 \, \text{mm}$

4. $0.004 \times 100^3 \times 10^3 = 4\,000\,000 \, \text{mm}^3$

Exam corner

1. Cube has side length $\sqrt[3]{216\,000} = 60 \, \text{cm} = 0.6 \, \text{m}$

Surface area of cube = $0.6 \times 0.6 \times 6 = 2.16 \, \text{m}^2$

Each tin of paint covers $2 \, \text{m}^2$, so 2 tins are needed.

1 mark for finding side length; 1 mark for converting units; 1 mark for surface area; 1 mark for correct answer. Total 4 marks.

2. Ratio of surface area $A : B$ is $30 : 270 = 1 : 9$

Ratio of length $A : B$ is $\sqrt{1} : \sqrt{9} = 1 : 3$

1 mark for ratio of surface areas in lowest form; 1 mark for any correct method to find ratio of lengths; 1 mark for correct answer. Total 3 marks.

3. Volume of smaller cone : volume of larger
cone $= \frac{1}{8} : 1 = 1 : 8$
Radius of smaller cone : radius of larger cone $= 1 : 2$
Therefore, radius of smaller cone $= 12 \div 2 = 6$
***1 mark** for correct ratio of volumes; **1 mark** for linking
SF of volume to radius; **1 mark** for correct answer.
Total 3 marks.*

Pages 126–127, Applying sine & cosine rules

Check-up box

1. 270°
2. 180° + 73° = 253°
3. South-east is a bearing of 135°, so return bearing is
180° + 135° = 315°

Exam corner

1. Label unknown angles and side.
To find side b, angle B is needed.
Use sine rule to first find angle A

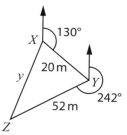

$\frac{\sin 74°}{12} = \frac{\sin A}{4}$
$\sin A = \frac{4 \sin 74°}{12}$
$A = 18.6883...°$
$B = 180 - 18.6883... - 74 = 87.3116...°$
Use this to find side b
$\frac{b}{\sin 87.3116...°} = \frac{12}{\sin 74°}$
$b = \frac{12 \sin 87.3116...°}{\sin 74°} = 12.47\,\text{m (to 2 dp)}$
Total length of fence $= 12.47 + 4 + 12 = 28.47\,\text{m}$
***1 mark** for attempt to use sine rule; **1 mark** for $\frac{4 \sin 74}{12}$;*
***1 mark** for finding angle 87.3(11...); **1 mark** for using
sine rule again (or cosine rule) to find unknown side;*
***1 mark** for correct answer. Total 5 marks.*
*Note that there are alternative methods (e.g. using cosine
rule and method for solving quadratics).*

2. a

Angle $XYZ = 360° - 242° - 50° = 68°$
Use cosine rule to find unknown side, y
$y^2 = 52^2 + 20^2 - (2 \times 20 \times 52 \times \cos 68°)$
$y^2 = 3104 - 779.181... = 2324.818...$
$y = 48.22\,\text{m (to 2 dp)}$
Total distance walked $= 48.22 + 20 + 52 = 120.22\,\text{m}$
***1 mark** for finding angle XYZ; **1 mark** for using
cosine rule; **1 mark** for correct value for y^2; **1 mark** for
correct value of y; **1 mark** for correct total distance. Total
5 marks.*

b 20 m = 2000 cm
2000 ÷ 1000 = 2
X to Y will be 2 cm.
***1 mark** for correct answer.*

Pages 128–129, Tricky probability questions

Check-up box

1. $0.6 \times \frac{2}{3} = 0.4$ or equivalent
2. P(doesn't rain) $= 1 - \frac{3}{x}$
$= \frac{x - 3}{x}$

Exam corner

1. a Number of red socks $= 2 \times 3 = 6$
Number of black socks $= 1 \times 3 = 3$
Total number of socks $= 9 + 6 + 3 = 18$

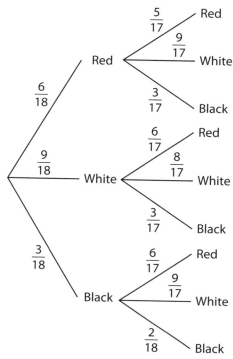

***1 mark** for tree diagram with $\frac{6}{18}$, $\frac{9}{18}$ and $\frac{3}{18}$ correct, or
equivalent; **1 mark** for denominator 17 on second set of
branches; **1 mark** for completely correct tree diagram.
Total 3 marks.*

b P(two red) $= \frac{6}{18} \times \frac{5}{17} = \frac{30}{306}$
P(two white) $= \frac{9}{18} \times \frac{8}{17} = \frac{72}{306}$
P(two black) $= \frac{3}{18} \times \frac{2}{17} = \frac{6}{306}$
P(two same colour) $= \frac{30}{306} + \frac{72}{306} + \frac{6}{306} = \frac{108}{306}\left(= \frac{6}{17}\right)$
***1 mark** for multiplying along branches; **1 mark** for
correct answer (or equivalent fraction).*

2. a

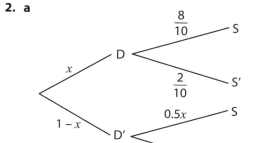

***1 mark** for first set of branches with x and $1 - x$; **1 mark**
for $\frac{8}{10}$ and $\frac{2}{10}$ (or equivalent) on second set of branches;*
***1 mark** for $0.5x$ and $1 - 0.5x$ on second set of branches;*
***1 mark** for completely correct tree diagram. Total 4 marks.*

b $(1 - x)(0.5x)$

1 mark for correct answer.

c $x \times \frac{2}{10} = 0.002$

$2x = 0.02, x = 0.01$

Probability that a person has the disease $= x = 0.01$

$\left(\text{or } \frac{1}{100}\right)$

1 mark for equating correct multiplication along branches to 0.002; *1 mark* for correct solution.

OXFORD
UNIVERSITY PRESS

Great Clarendon Street, Oxford, OX2 6DP, United Kingdom

Oxford University Press is a department of the University of Oxford.

It furthers the University's objective of excellence in research, scholarship, and education by publishing worldwide. Oxford is a registered trade mark of Oxford University Press in the UK and in certain other countries

British Library Cataloguing in Publication Data
Data available

978-1-38-200647-7

10 9 8 7 6 5 4 3 2 1

Paper used in the production of this book is a natural, recyclable product made from wood grown in sustainable forests.

The manufacturing process conforms to the environmental regulations of the country of origin.

Printed in the United Kingdom by Bell and Bain Ltd, Glasgow

Acknowledgements
Author: Katie Wood
Series Editor: Naomi Bartholomew-Millar
Editorial team: Dom Holdsworth, Matteo Orsini Jones (Haremi Ltd), Rosie Day

With thanks to Paul Hunt, Jemma Sherwood, Ross Everson and Jane Roth for their contributions.
The publisher would like to thank the following for permission to use copyright material:

Cover illustrations: Cristina Romero Palma / Shutterstock, Rachael Arnott / Shutterstock

Artwork by Q2A Media Services Pvt. Ltd.

Although we have made every effort to trace and contact all copyright holders before publication this has not been possible in all cases. If notified, the publisher will rectify any errors or omissions at the earliest opportunity.

Links to third party websites are provided by Oxford in good faith and for information only. Oxford disclaims any responsibility for the materials contained in any third party website referenced in this work.